My Runaway Summer

Peace, Love, and Rock 'n' Roll

Best-Selling Author

LARRY SCHARDT

Year of the Book
135 Glen Avenue
Glen Rock, PA 17327

ISBN: 978-1-64649-156-8 (print)
ISBN: 978-1-64649-265-7 (trade paperback)
ISBN: 978-1-64649-157-5 (ebook)

This book is a work of creative nonfiction. It recounts the author's best recollections and present memories of the summer of 1970. Some events have been compressed, reconstructed, or modified. Certain names and features have been changed. Dialogue has been reconstructed.

The use of certain words like "chicks," "girls," and "man" reflect the flavor of American slang used during the late 1960s and early 1970s. They were never intended to be derogatory.

Proceeds donated to shelters for runaway youth.

To Gail Brittenburg,
with love and appreciation.
Your tireless effort, editing, research,
love, and encouragement
made this book possible.
Endless thanks!

In loving memory and gratitude to
Edward and Mercedes Schardt,
my two greatest teachers,
both of whom molded me
into the person I am today.

Hippie*:

An idealistic dreamer with an eternally young heart and a free spirit, who promotes good and shares positivity. A hippie lives and believes in peace, love, kindness, and freedom.

A hippie can have long hair, wear unconventional clothes, and/or sport a headband, but those things are not necessary. A hippie is a hippie on the inside and radiates love from their heart and soul, no matter what they look like on the outside.

A hippie doesn't conform to the establishment (aka "The Man") that promotes war, hate, greed, control, and animosity.

Hippies are united by their idealism, gentle spirits, and love of music (especially Rock 'n' Roll... or whatever makes them rock!)

*Larry Schardt's definition

Reflections of the Era

"Yes, 'HIPPIE' can mean you were a free spirit from 1965 to 1975. It can also mean you love life, believe in peace, and love music at any age." —*Unknown*

"The '60s was one of the first times the power of music was used by a generation to bind them together." —*Neil Young*

"If someone thinks that love and peace is a cliche that must have been left behind in the '60s, that's his problem. Love and peace are eternal." —*John Lennon*

"For me, the lame part of the '60s was the political part, the social part. The real part was the spiritual part." —*Jerry Garcia*

"When the power of love overcomes the love of power, the world will know peace." —*Jimi Hendrix*

"The free soul is rare, but you know it when you see it— basically, because you feel good, very good, when you are near or with them." —*Charles Bukowski*

"Like the Arthurian years at Camelot, the '60s constituted a breakthrough, a fleeting moment of glory, a time when a significant little chunk of humanity briefly realized its moral potential and flirted with its neurological destiny, a collective spiritual awakening that flared brilliantly until the barbaric and mediocre impulses of the species drew tight once more the curtains of darkness." —*Tom Robbins*

"Knock on the door to my soul, and you will find an ageless hippie with a Rock 'n' Roll heart and a never-ending hope for peace." —*Unknown*

"Hippie is the one who embraces life to the fullest and promotes peace, love, and happiness." —*Unknown*

"The thing the '60s did was to show us the possibilities and the responsibility that we all had. It wasn't the answer. It just gave us a glimpse of the possibility." —*John Lennon*

Contents

1 | Aquarius...
My Generation

Summer 1970, Pittsburgh, Pennsylvania

Peace and love were everywhere. Everywhere... except at home.

Dad slapped me across my face and slammed me against the wall. Again. My head ricocheted off the plaster. Splitting pain. Lights out. Total blackness.

An instant later my nerve endings blasted with a violent eruption of stars, fireworks, and colors. My left cheek stung from the blow. My head pounded. I refused to cry. I wouldn't give Dad the extra pleasure of thinking he'd won.

"You gawd damned son-of-a-bitching bastard. You think you know everything? You worthless punk."

"At least I have a job."

He slapped me again.

I was fifteen years old and the Woodstock Nation and Age of Aquarius were in full swing. Peace, kindness, and harmony unified the Love Generation. Magic filled the air. Flower Power meant resisting "The Man," and Rock 'n' Roll provided the perfect soundtrack.

Home was a volatile powder keg wired to erupt. I lived in constant fear. I never knew when Dad was going to transform from the mellow persona of Dr. Jekyll into the raging lunatic, Mr. Hyde. No one knew when an explosion was coming. Out of nowhere, Dad's unprovoked outrage would destroy any sense of peace at home. Alcohol only served to intensify his tumultuous blowups.

At that age, I never understood why... and why only me? Why not my brothers or sisters? Why couldn't my father love me? What was wrong with me?

1

When I needed to break loose, Mt. Lebanon Park was just a ten-minute run down the hill and through the woods. "The Park" was a well-known gathering place for hippies in Pittsburgh. Long-hair, peace-signs, bellbottoms, incense, tie-dye, and beads abounded! Hugs, smiles, and cheer were everywhere. Rock 'n' Roll filled the air. My tribe. My music. My heaven... My safe place.

Before Dad had a chance to hit me again, my survival instinct kicked in. Without thinking, I ducked to my right, around my enraged father, and raced out the front door.

Was it the dark skies or the tears that clouded my vision? My legs couldn't move fast enough as I sprinted toward the trees that separated me from the park.

Out of breath, once safely into the woods, I rested on a log. My head throbbed and a torrent of sobs erupted. Off in the distance, echoing up the valley from the park below, a faint Bob Dylan's voice declared "The times, they are a-changin'."

I didn't know which was worse... the physical abuse at home or the mental torture I put myself through afterward. I lived with a dark black cloud hanging over my head, constantly tormented by negative thoughts... *Why did he hate me? What did I do wrong? Why didn't he love me like the rest of my eight brothers and sisters?* Only me. He never hit anyone else. Thank heavens.

No matter what I did, it was never enough. Why did he think I was worthless? It would be so much better for me to just leave... but where would I go? Get away from Dad. Give my family peace. I just had to get out. Escape! Escape! Escape!

My thoughts drifted 2,600 miles west, to the Haight-Ashbury district of San Francisco... my dream trip. If I was there, I could enjoy a life of peace, love, and happiness with the hippies. I could live free, meet my Flower Girl, and live happily ever after.

It was only a dream. It was one thing to fantasize about escape, to dream of running away, and dream of being with the perfect girl, but another thing entirely to go through with it.

Still, the hatred I felt from my father wouldn't let go. It was a prison I carried around in my head wherever I went.

I took deep breaths to calm myself and headed down toward Mt. Lebanon Park, less than half a mile from home. My escape was always temporary. At the end of the evening I'd have to return, never knowing if Dad would be waiting, prepared for battle.

I stepped from the woods into the park... my welcome place. The music got clearer as I made my way down the hill toward what we called "The Circle." I wandered through the small groups of people celebrating life, sitting on the hill, on the swings, or in a picnic pavilion. Some played guitars, some were lost in conversation, others laughed hysterically.

I spotted Reverend Bill, our park mentor, at the same time he saw me. He flashed me the peace sign. When I reached him no words were spoken. My face said it all.

"Looks like you and your father've been at it again." His tone was sympathetic.

"Yeah. I need to run away."

He'd heard it all before. It was always the same. One more night of abuse. One more night of escape. One more night of temporary relief.

Reverend Bill did his best to cheer me. "I know you're going through tough times right now, Larry. But remember, you can't run away from your problems."

"This time I'm really going to do it."

His firm hand pressed down on my shoulder. "You need to work it out. Focus on school. Have fun with your brothers, or spend time with your friends."

A brave me said, "I'm going to San Francisco."

I left Bill and circulated among friends hanging out around the park. The speakers on top of Al's van blasted Jimi Hendrix playing "All Along the Watchtower." I joined the dozen or so friends, dancing around the van and jammed along on my air guitar. Fingers strummed imaginary fingerboards, faces contorted with each high note, smiles overflowed.

3

There was nothing like phenomenal Rock 'n' Roll to lift my spirits. Music, friends, and the park...

"Get Together" came on.

"Larry!" Rebecca yelled from across the parking lot. She always brightened my day. I made my way over to where she was dancing. Her happy steps came to a halt when she saw my swollen cheek. She pulled me into a tight hug. "You still thinking about running away?" she whispered into my ear.

"Oh yeah! I just gotta get away from this place. Well, not this place, just my dad." The thought of living the hippie dream in Haight-Ashbury was never far from my mind. I wanted to live peace, love, and freedom. I wanted to flee, but deep inside I knew I'd never have the nerve.

"Hey, maybe we can hitch out to California together after graduation," Rebecca teased. "Maybe there's a band that needs a beautiful female singer."

"Yeah... let's do it," I said, knowing it would never happen. Graduation was still two tough years away. I doubted I could last that long.

The constant battle went on in my head. Leave or stay? Leave or stay? Leave or stay? Staying meant more beatings. Leaving meant freedom. Escape was always at the top of my mind.

"Hey Rebecca, can I walk you home tonight?"

"Sure. I gotta go see Amy. See you around 11:00?"

I made my way through the circle, caught up with friends, and air-jammed to great bands... Santana, The Grateful Dead, Jefferson Airplane, Big Brother & the Holding Company...

Rebecca and I found each other at the appointed hour. We walked shoulder to shoulder, winding our way toward her house through the tree-lined suburban streets. She became my sounding board while I griped about my father.

"Where is your mom through all of this?" she asked.

"Working."

"She has a job?"

"Three or four, actually. She works night shift at Mellon Bank downtown. She's a keypunch operator. She also retouches negatives and keeps books."

"What about your dad? Where does he work?"

"He doesn't. He just sits on his butt and watches TV all day."

Rebecca stopped walking. "Where does he get money to go out drinking?"

"He steals my paper route and grass cutting money. He also robs Judy and Mom when he can't find my money." I could hear the edge in my voice.

"Wow! So, he steals *your* money, goes out and gets drunk, and comes home and beats you up. I'd run away, too! You've been talking about running away to Haight-Ashbury forever. Do you think you will?"

I hesitated. A thousand thoughts bounced through my head. "Sure would be nice. I don't want to let my mom down though. And I'd miss my family. I'd have to find someone to take my paper routes. But it's scary to be home. I don't really know."

Rebecca said, "Haight Ashbury sounds cool. I know I'd never be brave enough to just take off."

"Me either. It's just nice dreaming about it," I answered, swallowing hard.

We stood out in front of her house talking. At 11:45, all sense of calm left me. "It's getting late. I need to get home." I gave Rebecca a quick hug and fled.

At midnight—Dad's bidden curfew—my insides twisted. Like always, I never wanted to go back, but I didn't want to give him one more excuse to hate me.

I was scared to be late. Scared to go home. Scared not to go home. Where would I go with my life? Where would I ever find peace? Would I ever really run away and find my freedom?

I prayed Dad would be asleep by the time I walked in.

The lights were on. The TV blared. I braced myself for another confrontation. I turned the doorknob...

Used with permission. Syda_Productions ID 99547224 / Depositphotos.com

2 | Gimme Shelter

My prayers were answered. Dad was slumped in his chair, sound asleep. Whew! I snuck by and climbed the stairs to get some sleep myself.

The shrill ring of the alarm clock came too soon. With one eye opened, I dragged my legs out from under the sheets and sat on the edge of the bed. My hand slammed the top of the clock to shut it off. Still tired, I knew I had to get moving. My customers would be waiting for their morning paper.

I heard Dad's snores from downstairs as I slipped my T-shirt over my head.

"Fritz! Wake up!" I whispered as I shook my brother's shoulder. "We need to do the papers. I'll check to see if Judy and Eric are up. Step on it, we don't want to be late. All of you meet me in the front yard."

Standing at the top of the steps I listened for other sounds. Time was ticking, I had no choice but to go downstairs. *The Pittsburgh Post-Gazette* needed to be delivered. Dad was still in a deep sleep. I held my breath and crept out the door.

I longed for escape. I yearned for a happy-go-lucky carefree Tom Sawyer life of adventure. I knew something had to change. I just had no idea how to go about doing it.

I knew I couldn't do anything until I graduated, which seemed like an eternity away. The constant battle in my head continued. I needed to stay, yet I needed to go. The world buzzed about the whole hippie scene. Peace, love, and kindness. What could be better?

My thoughts went wild... I dreamed of happiness on the "green grass" of the other side. I dreamed I'd move away, find a job, and send the extra money back home. I knew Mom could use every penny. Besides, it would be one less mouth to feed...

and it sure would make things more peaceful at home. Dad didn't want me there anyway.

The summer continued. The abuse continued. The taunting continued.

My dream of escaping to Haight-Ashbury consumed my thoughts.

Fourth of July fireworks were a far cry more enjoyable than the fireworks at home. A few days after the bombs burst in air, I went to the park. The picnic table buckled under the weight of my friends who sat huddled on top. Everyone was talking at the same time. Music to my ears.

"Did you hear John is looking for someone to hitchhike to New Jersey with him?" one asked.

New Jersey may have been in the opposite direction from San Francisco, but it seemed like a great place to start... just to get away.

In an instant, a zillion thoughts flooded my brain. My Tom Sawyer spirit kicked in. Should I go?

Used with permission. Depositphotos.com

3 | Hitchin' a Ride

I found John sitting on a table near the swings. In typical guy form, he was hunched over, smoking a cigarette and staring at his feet. Smoke circled his head. John was a loner, and watched me intently as I casually sat on the open space next to him.

We sat in silence for a few seconds. "Hey, man," I said when I got the nerve. "I heard you were looking for someone to go with you to Ocean City. I'm thinking of going. What's it like, man?"

"It's such a cool place. I'm going to stay all summer. Got a great place to crash," John said.

"They have any jobs there?" I asked.

"Jobs are easy to come by. You wanna come along? You'll love it," John added.

"I'm in," I blurted. "When are you going?"

"Today."

"Today?" I balked.

"So you wanna come?"

It was all happening so fast. "Yeah, it's just what I need. What time?"

"Meet me right here at 3:30," he said.

I looked at my watch and shouted, "An hour!" My heart skipped a beat.

"We've got to get on the road, man!"

And like that, my life changed. I committed. No turning back.

I jumped off that table and raced home. I grabbed a brown paper grocery bag from the broom closet on my way through the kitchen and hurdled my way to the second floor. My pulse hammered with each step.

I threw the bag on my bed and looked around. What would I do now? What should I take? My toothbrush, clothes. What

9

else? My hands became sweaty and a knot formed in my throat. "Am I really doing this?"

I had become so focused on escaping that I blanked on the details. I didn't think about what I would eat, where I would stay, or what I would do for money.

All I thought about was getting out.

Then it hit me... if I wasn't home for dinner, Mom would worry. I decided to write her a note.

"Dear Mom – If you love me please don't call the cops."

Used with permission. Pixabay.com

With the bag in my hand I glanced around my room one last time. I heard the buzz of the can opener from the top step. Mom was putzing around in the kitchen.

I thought I'd better sneak out through the garage. I knew that if she took one look at me and the bag, she'd know something was up and ask me a lot of questions.

My knees trembled. My feet clung to the steps like magnets, sticking to each one, trying my best to get to the bottom without being noticed. My hands shook as I fumbled with the doorknob. I cracked open the door in slow motion hoping the squeak wouldn't give me away. But it was louder than I thought.

I froze...

So close...

Silence...

Whew!

I shut the door behind me, and ran. I didn't look back.

I reached the park at 3:30 and John was sitting on the picnic table just like he said he would be. "Good, you're here. We've got about 400 miles to hitch. We've gotta get going."

He led the way. Four hundred miles? Wow. Two fifteen-year-olds ready to discover the world.

We walked through the park to Cedar Boulevard and stuck out our thumbs. Within minutes a blue Volkswagen pulled over. What phenomenal luck! We ran to the car and opened the door.

Used with permission. Pennsylvania Turnpike Photo Archives.

"Hi, Larry," a lady said as I peered into the vehicle.

I recognized the voice. I looked up and popped my head into the door of the Volkswagen. Dang! It was my neighbor. I was busted.

With a nervous smile, I said, "Hi, Mrs. Sullivan." So much for our short-lived luck.

"So where are you boys going?" she asked.

I paused. My heart rate accelerated.

Enthusiastically John intervened. "We're going to visit some friends at the shore."

"Hop in," Mrs. Sullivan said. "Where can I drop you off?"

"Can you get us near the turnpike?" John asked.

"Sure. I'm on my way to teach class at Pitt. That's in my direction. I can get you partway there. No problem."

She concentrated on the road ahead, but a few times her eyes wandered to my feet where the brown bag laid. It made me jittery, afraid she didn't believe our story.

"Does your mom know where you're going?"

"Sure," I said with a cracked voice. Okay, so I stretched the truth a bit... I did leave her a note.

Mrs. Sullivan went beyond her normal route and took us all the way to the turnpike.

"Larry, do you have any money?"

Her question reminded me that I didn't have any cash at all. "Not right now, but I'm going to find a job on the boardwalk."

"Let me see how much money I have." She reached into her purse and took out her wallet, handing me two dollars. "I didn't get to the bank yet today. This is all I have, but maybe it can hold you over. Have fun and... be careful."

"Thanks." I closed the door.

John and I waved goodbye and watched our last connection with home drive off. As her car moved into the distance, I folded the bills and buried them in my jeans pocket. *Thank you, Mrs. Sullivan!*

We walked up the turnpike ramp in the blistering July sun and stuck out our thumbs. Just another 365 miles to Ocean City, New Jersey...

John looked over. "I sure hope we get a ride before the cops drive by."

Used with permission. Depositphotos.com

4 | I'm Free

John and I stuck out our right arms, thumbs up to traffic. Despite the suffocating heat, I shivered. Back and forth, back and forth, my thoughts ping-ponged... one minute I dreamed of the perfect life that I was sure laid ahead—freedom, a new job, pretty girls! Then boom... an adrenaline jolt would steal away the moment and plunge me into the plague of paranoia— cops, busted, adults, "The Man"... the dreaded "establishment."

Getting caught and being sent back home was not an option I cared to face. Any sign of a policeman shot currents of panic through my veins, always there, lurking at the edge of my thoughts. Just in case, I looked around for an escape route, a place to flee, a place to hide, a place for shelter. But there weren't any. On that vast expanse of barren concrete there would be no running away.

Then my thoughts wandered back to my cherished freedom. Back and forth... back and forth... back and forth!

Thank heavens, it only took a few minutes to get our next lift. A kind, older woman picked us up. John sat up front.

"Hop in. My boys hitchhike back and forth to Penn State, so I'll try to help you."

In the back seat I was excited to be heading one step closer to our goal. This woman reminded me of Mom. I wondered what would be happening at home right now. I bet Mom was making dinner and everyone else would be outside playing kickball.

This woman did what any mother would do. She lectured us about the dangers of hitchhiking.

We must have looked hungry because she offered us a big bag of Wise potato chips from the grocery sack beside me on the back seat. It made a delicious dinner.

That ride inched us closer to our destination. The closer we got, the more nervous I felt. I wondered if Mrs. Sullivan called Mom. Did Mom find the note and call the cops?

We stood on the turnpike entrance ramp in Somerset. Time ticked by. Thoughts ricocheted. The sun sank closer toward the evening horizon. After about fifteen antsy minutes, a guy in a big black Dodge slowed down, looked us over, and swerved onto the shoulder. His fast move made us leery.

Sure looked like an unmarked police car... Was it "The Man?"

Used with permission. Depositphotos.com and Pennsylvania Turnpike Commission.

5 | Goin' Up the Country

The black car idled, waiting. I gave John a what-the-heck-do-we-do-now look. He returned the same. Were we busted?

We hesitated, then proceeded with caution. With no place to run, we had no choice.

When we got closer to the car, a man leaned over the front seat and rolled down the passenger side window. "Are you boys coming or what?" the man in a gray suit asked. Then he broke the ice and smiled. "Where you headed?"

"Ocean City."

"Get in. I can get you as far as Reading."

"Thanks, man."

John grabbed the front seat again. I slid across the white vinyl upholstery into the back. I mentally planned an escape route, just in case. After I closed the door, my hand remained on the handle. I don't know why... it's not as if I would jump out of a speeding car on the highway.

"My name's Tom," he said, glancing in the rearview mirror to pull out onto the road. "When I was your age, I used to love to go to the beach. We went to Wildwood a lot. You ought to check it out."

His encouragement and enthusiasm put me somewhat at ease but I didn't let my guard down. I still had my doubts. He was an adult after all.

"You've got a ways to go yet."

Time passed. John and Tom did most of the talking while I listened and let the hot highway breeze blow through my hair. The more they talked, the more I relaxed.

"We'll get to Reading about 9:00," Tom said. "It'll be almost dark by then. Ocean City is at least another two hours away. But there won't be much traffic at night."

I shuddered at the thought of being stranded. Even if we did get a ride, what would we do when we got to the beach that late? Either way, two teenage kids would stick out like glowing neon signs. What were we thinking when we left Pittsburgh so late?

I couldn't imagine anything worse than being marooned at night on a ramp in a faraway city. Except maybe getting busted. Strangers in a strange land...

Just knowing that Reading was still hours away caused the butterflies in my stomach to multiply. My leg jiggled and no matter how hard I pressed down on my knee, it refused to stop. Visions of standing on a concrete runway—helpless, abandoned, and in the dark—horrified me.

But the beach called... a new beginning was ahead.

More fears crept in—the cops, getting caught, being sent home.

Tom and John continued their conversation up front. I sat in the back half paying attention. I still wasn't sure about Tom. I suspected he might be an undercover officer. Probably just paranoia. I simply couldn't trust adults and I had a nagging feeling that every cop out there knew I was a runaway.

The hot July evening breeze coming through the window made me blink. The countryside sped by, dotted with barns, farmhouses, wide open fields, and a lot of black and white cows.

Used with permission. dcwcreations/Depositphotos.com

Evening shadows got longer. Sunset wasn't far away. Dusk came. My thoughts intensified with worst-case scenarios. Stranded? Starved? Busted?

Tom said, "Hey, I've got an idea. There's a service plaza before we get to the Reading exit. Why don't we stop there? You can ask around to see if anyone can give you a lift. That way you wouldn't have to worry about getting stuck outside overnight."

That sounded like a wonderful idea.

Until we pulled into the rest area.

My stomach twisted when I saw two police cruisers parked at the entrance of the Howard Johnson's restaurant. Was this a set-up?

Used with permission. Pennsylvania Turnpike Authority.

6 | Magic Carpet Ride

I lagged behind Tom as we walked toward the restaurant. I wondered why cops were parked in the lot. Was Tom ready to hand us over?

The disgusting smell of diesel filled the air. Familiar rumbles of idling trucks were interrupted by garbled words coming over the police radios in the empty cruisers. It was icing on my melting cake of despair...

The glass doors led us into the lobby. On our right were two officers seated at the lunch counter. They stopped talking when we approached the stools. One officer's eyes burned in my direction. Sweat beaded on my forehead. I stared at the floor hoping he wouldn't notice me.

I sucked in a gulp of air once we were past them, relieved that they were not looking for me. Their attention turned to a radio alert. They rushed to pay their bill at the register, and took off, sirens blaring!

Tom went over to the cigarette machine. John looked up at the black velvet menu board hanging above the cash register. I didn't have any money to spare so I didn't bother. Even though the cops were gone, I kept my head down, wanting to disappear. Still nervous, I did my best to act calm so I would not be noticed.

Tom came back with a pack of Marlboros. He offered us each a cigarette, then said his goodbyes, wishing us luck. There we were, on our own again. How long could two teenage boys linger at a rest area and not arouse suspicion?

John and I sat on the red plastic swivel counter stools with our backs toward the door. He ordered a Coke. I ordered a glass of water. I couldn't afford to waste ten cents of my two-dollar fortune on a soda.

I looked across the waitress aisle at the ice cream menu etched on the mirror above the dessert bar. My stomach churned. John was a regular hitchhiker so he had experience talking to people. I was more timid.

John got up and made his way around the restaurant asking people for a ride. I sat and waited for my water. I could see the disappointment on his face as person after person turned him down. My insides hollowed.

Then I heard a commotion... I swirled around on my stool to look...

Used with permission. Pennsylvania Turnpike Photo Archives.

Two older teenage guys bounded through the door, laughing and carrying on. I smiled and spun back to the counter. I continued to watch John go from booth to booth.

After a bit the boys came and sat at the counter to my left. They waved and said, "Hey."

I flashed them the peace sign. "Hi."

Their voices projected with excitement. They were jabbering on about going to the shore. The waitress took their order.

A disappointed John slunk back over and sat to my right. "No luck."

When the waitress saw John come back she brought a tray with four Cokes—two for the other guys and two for us.

"I'm sorry. I didn't order a Coke."

She peered at me, grabbed the glass, and dumped it down the sink right in front of me. My empty stomach growled in disbelief.

Used with permission. everett225/Depositphotos.com

I elbowed John and nodded in the boys' direction. "Those guys are going to the beach."

John beamed. "Hey man, where you headed?"

"We're going to Ocean City."

"Oh wow, so are we! But we need a ride. Can you give us a lift?"

They talked about it and said, "Sure. I think we can squeeze you in."

"Thanks." We introduced ourselves.

Eric and Joe became our fast friends. We talked about our favorite subjects—the beach, the fun, the girls. They were in no hurry to finish their burgers. My foot shook up and down. We couldn't ask them to speed it up, although my thoughts were directed that way. Anxiety blasted through every pore.

Time drew on... the nasty waitress stared.

At long last, Eric and Joe finished eating. John and I scrunched way down and twisted our six-foot frames into the back seat of the small, four-door Corvair, which I swear was not designed for anyone over four feet tall. Cramped but happy, we were off!

Eric and Joe had just graduated from high school and were on their way to the beach to celebrate. A sliver of the moon hung in the darkening sky. It would be after midnight by the time we got to Ocean City. Eric and Joe talked about sleeping on the beach.

John said, "But you can't crash on the beach when it's closed. The beach patrol will catch you for sure."

I felt lucky that John had friends for us to stay with.

Or so I thought.

Used with permission. Corvair 1960 by Hugo-90 licensed under CC bY 2.0.

7 | America...
Counting Cars

Since John had been back and forth to Ocean City earlier that summer, he spoke with the voice of wisdom. He was our tour-guide "authority." After he advised our new friends against the perils of sleeping on the beach, Joe said, "I guess we'll just have to sleep in the car."

John snapped, "That's just as bad. The cops walk up and down the streets and check every vehicle. Every night."

After a long silent pause, Joe followed with a defeated answer. "We have no other choice."

John's voice reeked with sarcasm. "Okay. Don't listen to me. Go ahead and get caught."

I was surprised and embarrassed by his underhanded reply. But I was comforted knowing that John had a place for us to stay.

We exited the Pennsylvania Turnpike and got onto the Schuylkill Expressway. Even at night the traffic got heavier as we made our way through Philadelphia. The inky blackness of the river on our left reflected dots of light here and there.

As we got further east, the rolling hills flattened into the Atlantic City Expressway. It was a stark contrast from anything I'd ever seen. So different from the home I'd left behind.

Home. Mom would've already been at work. The older kids in the neighborhood were likely playing release, a team version of hide-n-seek. My younger brothers and sisters were probably saying their prayers and getting ready for bed.

By the time we turned south onto the Garden State Parkway, the air was heavy with the smell of the sea.

At long last... the exit sign for Somers Point/Ocean City came into view! My heart pumped. We were so close. Almost there. We crossed a miles-long bridge and pulled into town well past midnight. The wide open car windows allowed the sticky salt air to come in. It clung to my hair. But the ocean would have to wait. We still had to make it through the night.

The town was unlike anything back home. Lawns were sparse, more sand than grass. The place looked deserted, something out of an eerie horror movie like *Night of the Living Dead.*

A few blocks in, Eric found a parking space shadowed from the streetlights. He maneuvered the Corvair between other cars lining both sides of the long straight street.

John and I opened the back doors and climbed out. How wonderful to stand tall and stretch out the kinks and cramps in my neck, legs, and every other muscle in my body!

John immediately started walking away. He did a half turn and waved. "Thanks for the ride. My friends are waiting." He followed with, "Hey Larry, see you on the boardwalk tomorrow. You're on your own."

I stood in shock. "What?"

He ignored me and just kept walking.

What???

Used with permission. ChrisTefme/Depositphotos.com

8 | The Sound of Silence

Stunned, I watched John walk up the street. At the end of the block he turned the corner and disappeared. I stared at the empty sidewalk. The rug of hope pulled out from under me. My dreams were shattered.

Just like that my world fell apart. Deserted!

John was the one person I'd put all my trust into... every single bit of it. Now what? He had a reputation for being a master manipulator but I never figured he'd stick it to me. How could I have been so stupid?

I wanted to run, but my feet felt cemented to the pavement. I didn't even know where I was, or where to go. Where could I even run to? Now what?

I grabbed my clammy T-shirt and dragged it across my face, as much to wipe away the salt air as to hide my embarrassment and tears.

I finally gained enough composure to reach into the car to grab my bag. "Thank you, man." I flashed Eric and Joe the peace sign.

"Wait a minute? Where're you going?" Joe asked. "Why don't you stay with us in the car? At least you won't be on the streets."

Sleeping in the car was dangerous. But it beat the alternative. I would be with old friends. Old friends? Heavens, I'd known these guys for three or four whole hours!

I squeezed into the back seat, again. Eric was up front trying to balance on the bench seat behind the steering wheel and passenger door. Joe and I crunched into the back. He took the back half of the seat and I did my best to balance on the front of the sticky vinyl upholstery, part on the floor, part on the seat. I twisted. My body cramped. I stared up at the shaded roof panel.

The July air was thick. With the windows rolled up it felt like we were in an oven.

The odds were stacked against us. Would we make it through the night? Was that even possible? Tired as I was, I couldn't sleep. My mind would not shut off.

After all this way... would I ever see the ocean? Would the cops catch us? How would I get money? Where could I find a job? Where would I stay?

And man, was I ever hot, crunched... and hungry!

Over and over, my thoughts tumbled. I must have dozed off. Before I knew what was happening, a bright light beamed across my face. I froze, too terrified to open my eyes.

Used with permission. Depositphotos.com

My skin tingled. I blinked my eyes open. My weary and paranoid brain was playing tricks on me. The light turned out to be the sun. I laughed to myself.

We made it through the night! Daylight never looked so fabulous. I hoped today would be a better day. Maybe I'd even get to see the ocean. I laid still, stiff, and twisted. And wow, was it ever hot! On top of it all, my empty stomach reminded me that I needed food. I was famished.

Every muscle ached. I needed to untangle. My pretzeled body stuck to the vinyl seat. Torture! Thankfully, I didn't have to wait long.

"Anyone awake?" Joe whispered.

Eric answered from the front, "Yep."

"Me too."

We all unraveled, flung open the doors, got out, and stretched. It was only 5:30 A.M. We were all groggy.

"I'm dying. I need to get to the men's room." Joe grinned.

We grabbed our toothbrushes and walked a few blocks toward the boardwalk, searching for the public restrooms. But more than anything else and most important to me, my moment of glory was just ahead. I was almost there!

The ocean called from a couple blocks away. The closer we got, the more my adrenaline pumped. Every step brought me nearer to my dream. I raced up the stairs onto the wooden planks.

At last! There it was... my destination—the Atlantic Ocean extending beyond the horizon. Waves following waves crashed across the sandy beach.

I wanted to shout, "I'm here! I'm alive! I'm free!"

Eric and Joe kept plugging ahead. They pointed. "Bathrooms are over there."

I stood in a trance, mesmerized. Screaming seagulls startled me back to the moment. They were at war for something in a trash can.

I wandered up the boardwalk. I thought I was smart bringing a toothbrush, but when I got to the restroom, I realized that my friends were smarter. They brought toothpaste... and soap.

Eric laughed, handing me both. "Here, you might need these."

"Thanks a million!" Those guys were true blessings! They finished and went outside.

When I walked back out onto the slatted walkway there was no sign of Eric or Joe. Where the heck were those guys? Then my thoughts switched tracks. Panic set in. What would happen if I ran into John? What would I say?

And man, was I hungry!

Used with permission. Pixabay.com

9 | I'm a Girl Watcher

"Hey Larry, over here." Joe waved from a bench nearby, already ogling the beautiful girls. Then like little kids with new toys, the three of us explored the boardwalk.

Crashing waves on our left competed with squawking seagulls. The allure of bacon and eggs broke through the salty air when we passed the restaurants. Families flowed up and down like the waves. And there were more pretty girls than I ever imagined. My temporary home looked better by the minute.

The day awoke in front of us. Walkers and cyclists made their way up and down the boardwalk. Merchants rolled up their aluminum gates, ready to start their day. So many happy families. What would it be like to have a vacation?

We walked all the way past every shop and up to the end. By the time we got back to the heart of the boardwalk, the beaches were lined with blankets and umbrellas. Our eyes bulged trying to take in all the bikini-clad girls.

When we got to 8th Street, Joe said, "Enough walking. I'm heading to the beach to get a better look."

We raced each other down the steps. Eric and Joe plopped onto the sand and took in the sights.

I stripped off my shirt, flipped my sneakers into the sand, and headed to the ocean. Almost there, I stopped and rolled up my bellbottoms. I buried my toes in the cool wet water, leaned back and spread my arms wide, soaking in the magnificence of the sun... perched as if to fly. This was heaven... the sand, the ocean, the scenery... and my newfound friends.

The beach was bursting with people. Ah, fresh air, ocean breeze, more bikinis! The surf surrounded my legs and I basked in the celebration of life. I breathed in those glorious miraculous moments.

I turned and walked up to where Eric and Joe sat. They were so focused on their swimsuit judging contest they didn't even notice me. I followed their gaze. A pretty girl turned toward us and waved. Busted! We waved back to hide our embarrassment.

Time passed and our necks grew sore. Eric said, "Pop your eyes back in. Let's grab some food. My treat. All this girl watching is making me hungry."

Joe and I warmed a space on a bench along the boardwalk and waited for Eric. To my delight he came back with a half-dozen delicious glazed doughnuts—the perfect breakfast for starving teenagers.

We sat and devoured our meal, and made sure to point out sights as they walked by.

Used with permission. duplass/Depositphotos.com

When I took my last bite, Joe said, "We've gotta go. We've gotta pick a few things up and get to our motel. The guy told me we could check in at 10:00."

Eric crumpled the empty box and tossed it into the trash. "Larry, don't forget that your bag is in the car."

"Oh, yeah. Thanks for reminding me," I said.

As we walked toward the Corvair we pushed each other back and forth, comparing notes, doing our best to fulfill our role as teenage boys.

"She was smiling at me."

"No, she was smiling at me."

"No, no, no, she was smiling at me!"

"She's too old for you."

In the short time I had known them they became more like my big brothers.

We got to the car and opened the door. A balloon of heat escaped, blasted us, and just about knocked us over.

Joe reached in, grabbed my bag, and handed it to me. We shook hands. "Good luck! Be careful."

"Thank you."

Eric steered out of the parking space and headed down the road. My heart sank.

I held up the peace sign and watched them drive out of sight. My last touch of familiarity drove off. There I was, stranger in a strange land, again. Alone, again. Stranded, again.

Reality check! This was it. I had to get a job.

I turned and walked toward 9th Street and back to the boardwalk. I ambled up the steps.

When I was near the top I looked up. I wanted to run, but it was too late. The last person I wanted to see stood in front of me... waiting...

10 | The Flower Girl

There, in front of me... was... John.

He stood by the railing next to the steps and watched me. What in the world was I going to say to him? I didn't want to say anything.

When I got to the top he spoke first. "Hey man, where you been?" Like nothing had happened.

Lost for words, I paused. "I made it through the night... no thanks to you."

"Hey, at least you made it. No big deal." His tone dripped with sarcasm.

No big deal. No big deal? No big deal! My mind echoed his cold words.

Arguing with him wouldn't solve a thing. I didn't want to cause a scene on the boardwalk with hundreds of people around either. I changed the subject and threw my hands up. "So what's the plan for today?"

"I don't know about you, but I'm headed to New York," he said.

"New York?" I was baffled.

John said, "Yeah. That's why I came here. I wanted to meet up with George so we could hitch up there. There's a big Rock fest happening. That's the only reason I came. You wanna come along?"

"But you said we were going to get jobs and stay at your friend's place until we could get an apartment," I replied.

"So I lied. I don't need a job. I'd rather have fun. I'm heading to New York. No sweat off my back if you don't come."

My enthusiasm tanked. I felt like a fool. I'd put all my trust in John. What a con man! I'd rather be stuck alone in a place with a beach... and an ocean... and a boardwalk.

Just then a couple of cute girls in bikinis walked by... and you can't beat that scenery.

"John, I trusted you, man. You let me down. You think I want to hitchhike to New York with you? No way!"

"Your loss." His tone was ice cold.

"So I guess you don't really know where there are any jobs?" I asked.

"Yeah, you got it. I'm gone." He gave me the finger and walked away.

Wow! Now I really didn't know a soul in Ocean City.

I snapped back to the moment. I was standing next to Shriver's Candy Store. Through the huge picture window, I spotted a bin of Licorice Allsorts—my brother Fritz's favorite. *I wonder what he's doing right now...*

Was coming here a mistake?

Photo by author. Ocean City, NJ boardwalk.

No. As quick as the thought came, I did my best to erase it from my conflicted mind. Going back was not an option.

My heart was sick. I missed Fritz. I missed all my brothers and sisters. I missed Mom. I missed my friends. But go back? *No.*

I left to save myself. I'd escaped. I'd made the break. This was the toughest decision of my life.

I knew I should really let Mom know that I was safe though. I should tell her I was going to find a job and send money back home. But I needed to survive. I couldn't bear to hear her sad voice.

I needed to start looking for a job, but the short night's sleep was catching up with me. I was bushed, too tired to think. I decided to take a nap on the beach. Maybe that would clear my mind.

I turned from the candy store window and made my way to the steps across the boardwalk. There was a pavilion just ahead on my left. Groups of people milled around inside.

Before I went down the steps, I stopped and looked over. People were huddled in conversation... smiling, laughing, and carrying on. Guys had long hair. Gals adorned their flowing locks with flowers. Tie-dye, bellbottoms, the smell of patchouli... it was a hippie mecca.

The shelter buzzed with happiness. It was the Mt. Lebanon Park of Ocean City. I flashed the peace sign at no one in particular since almost everyone was busy doing what they were doing... except for one cute blonde girl with a white flower above her ear. She smiled and flashed the peace sign back at me.

I melted! In that instant, the world transformed into a better place.

Exhausted and much too shy to go over, I continued down the steps and laid on the beach below. I took off my shoes and my shirt and rolled up my bellbottoms to bask in the sun.

The sand was oven hot! I used my shirt for a towel and my paper bag for a pillow. I should've gone over and said hello. I wished I weren't so shy.

I dozed off. A strumming guitar woke me. At first I needed to get my bearings, forgetting that I was even at the beach. When my eyes opened, two beautiful blue eyes were looking down at me. It startled me and I quickly propped myself on one elbow. A tropical ocean breeze blew wisps of long blonde hair across a warm and welcoming face, decorated with a smile that dazzled.

It was her... the girl who had flashed me the peace sign. Before I knew it she was sitting cross-legged in front of me.

I sat upright and smiled a sheepish grin. "Hi!" I said.

At that moment, Ocean City came to life. I went from my black and white world of desperation to the full-spectrum kaleidoscope of awe.

Used with permission. redwine2001/Depositphotos.com

"Hi, I'm Anne."

"I'm Larry. Nice to meet you."

I felt like I couldn't get enough air. The perfect flower child was sitting right in front of me beaming as bright as the sun.

"You like music?"

"Yeah, I love Rock 'n' Roll."

"Great! I figured. That's my friend Tim playing up there. This afternoon a bunch of people will be getting together to jam." She strummed her air guitar. "I wanted to invite you."

"Thanks."

"You new around here? I've never seen you before."

"Just got here. I hitchhiked from Pittsburgh. Got in late last night. Slept in a car with some guys who picked me up."

"Wow! I can't believe you didn't get caught." She flinched. "The cops don't let you get away with anything here."

As quickly as she sat down, she jumped up and spun toward the ocean. "Hey, wanna take a walk?"

"Sure." I stood and did my best to anchor my feet onto the sand so I wouldn't float away. I had to remind myself to stay calm and cool. I left my paper bag and shirt.

She led the way. We speed-walked across the scorching beach and found relief at the edge of the ocean. The cool wet sand chilled our feet and the waves rolled across our ankles.

The world disappeared around us. There I was with the perfect girl. The perfect flower child.

"You hitchhiked. Why?" Anne asked.

"I had to escape. It was too dangerous at home... alcohol... violence... always worried that my dad might flip out. I just had to leave."

"So you hitched all this way alone?" Anne asked.

"No. This guy John was coming here. He needed someone to hitch with. He told me we could stay with his friends in Ocean City until we got an apartment. He told me we could easily find jobs. Sounded like a great idea at the time. But he lied. As soon as we got here, he took off."

"He left you by yourself? What a jerk." She shook her head. "Man..."

"Luckily, on our way, we got picked up by these two cool guys, Eric and Joe. I hung out with them for a while but they left to check into their motel. Things sure didn't turn out the way I expected. Not even close."

One question led into the next twenty. Time flowed... the blocks flowed... our talk flowed.

I was mesmerized by Anne's tender voice. She was so calm and cool.

On the other hand I questioned my every sentence and filled my head with self-doubt. Was I saying the right thing? She had captured my heart. I hoped she felt the same.

"So, does your mom know where you are?"

Surprised she had asked, I turned to look. At that moment, her eyes opened wider.

She stopped. Her voice quivered, "Oh my gawd. We're at the fishing pier. I didn't realize how far we'd walked." With a sudden turn, she headed back the way we came, quickening her pace. "Oh man, we've got to get back. He's going to be so mad."

"He?"

"Ocean City Fishing Pier" by PMillera4, licensed under CC BY-NC-ND 2.0.

11 | Dazed and Confused

We charged back down the beach like we were being chased by a lion. Anne was on a mission, and it looked like it wasn't a fun one. Her smile was gone. Her spirit was gone. Her chattiness was gone.

I tried to get her to talk. Her answers became clipped. My mind exploded with questions... *What's going on? What's she late for? And who's "he?"*

The rest of the trip was dazed, confused, and silent. Every so often the in and out of the waves brought me back to the ocean, but my confusion lingered.

By the time we got back to my waiting paper bag, I leaned over. Anne didn't stop. She just continued up the beach.

"Where're you going?" I asked.

She turned her head but kept walking. "Sorry. I've got to meet him at the music pier. I'll see you at the jam later." She flashed me the peace sign, winked, and charged forward.

My eyes followed her as she walked away. That jam couldn't happen fast enough.

When Anne was well out of sight, I ran down and jumped into the ocean to rinse off my hot and sweaty body. The waves washed over me. It wasn't a warm shower but it sure felt wonderful.

I got out and headed back to my bag, combing my fingers through my hair. I reached in and grabbed a clean T-shirt. My cotton bellbottoms dripped and dragged through the sand. I was prepared to start my job search... I sure hoped my pants would dry fast.

The effects of the two doughnuts had long worn off. Food became more important than a job. My stomach churned. Grub on the boardwalk was too expensive. I needed something—

something cheap. I would have to stretch my food supply as long as possible. A loaf of bread would be perfect.

I walked up the steps and over the boardwalk into town. A parking lot attendant gave me directions to the nearest grocery store, just a few blocks away. Once inside the Acme I went straight for the bread aisle and searched for the best bargain. The shelves were sparse. It was likely the only store nearby where vacationers could buy groceries. I grabbed a loaf of the store brand bread.

My thoughts were still focused on Anne. I wasn't paying much attention but I heard a couple of guys talking. Before I knew it, a cop came around the corner into my aisle. He stopped and looked me up and down.

I must have looked pathetic—soaking wet pants, crumpled brown paper bag under my arm. My thoughts had been so focused on Anne that I totally forgot about the police.

My gut instinct was to drop the bag and run. Thank heavens my rational mind took control. "Hello, sir." I swallowed.

"Hello, son." His eyes focused on my bag. "Whatcha got in there?"

"Clothes." I felt myself digging my own grave.

He laughed and looked down at my dripping bellbottoms. "I see you forgot a swimsuit." He laughed again, then grabbed a pack of cupcakes and walked away.

I let out a long grateful exhale. Thank you, God!

I decided I should splurge on a jar of peanut butter to go with the bread. I got in line to pay and hoped no one else could hear the grumbling noises from my stomach.

Used with permission. Depositphotos.com

"That will be 97 cents," the clerk announced as she placed the goods into a fresh brown paper bag. *Whew, 97 cents!* That two dollars sure wasn't going to go far.

I walked past the dumpster at the back of the store and across the parking lot. I sat on a curb ready to devour a couple of sandwiches. The void in my stomach was screaming.

I unscrewed the lid, excited to eat, but realized I didn't have a way to spread the peanut butter. I threw everything back in the bag, found a burger joint down the road, and picked up a full set of heirloom plastic utensils.

An empty bench called my name and I "cooked" myself a delicious meal. The first bite got stuck to the roof of my mouth. Peanut butter never tasted so good!

As I ate, visions of Anne showered my thoughts. That beautiful free-spirited flower girl! Walking up the beach with her was heaven... Watching her walk away was hell.

I couldn't wait for the afternoon jam session. I would get to see her again... I was smitten, yet confused.

I savored my last bite. I took my worldly possessions from that ripped paper bag and put them into the new one. I was careful to place the loaf of bread on top.

Packed, satisfied, and determined, I headed back to the boardwalk intent on getting a job. I started at the low end and went from ice cream stands, to stores, to pizza places. No luck.

"We're not hiring." "The boss isn't here." "Come back next week." "How old are you?"

John deceived me. Jobs were *not* easy to come by. Thank heavens, daydreams of Anne drifted back into my thoughts and rescued me.

After struggling with a few painful rejections I quit for the day and headed to Shriver's Pavilion. As I came closer, the music, singing, and laughter got louder. The rush of excitement swelled in my chest and a smile spread from ear to ear. *Anne should be here*, I thought as a giggle forced its way out.

I went into the shelter. Benches lined its perimeter. A couple dozen hippies gathered in groups. A few guitar players jammed. Folks swayed to the rhythm and drummed on the benches. Songs filled the air.

But no Anne.

I looked around and searched. Where was she?

I stood out in the open, hoping she would see me. Most of the people nodded, smiled, and flashed the peace sign as a way of greeting. It really was like Mt. Lebanon Park had come to the boardwalk. I'd found my tribe, but I didn't know anyone. I was an outcast without a friend. *Where was Anne?*

Reminders of home persisted. The heartbreak. The people. The music.

I drifted in and out of confusion. The musicians treated us to familiar songs that dreamed me back home... Bob Dylan's "Blowin' in the Wind" and the new Beatles tune, "Let It Be." Their music tugged at my heart.

The more I looked for Anne the more isolated I felt. Over and over, I searched up and down the boardwalk. Still no Anne. *Did I do something wrong? I hope she's okay.* As usual, my head filled with insecurity and doubt.

My worry broke when I heard the perfect song. The entertainers strummed into the classic tune, "San Francisco (be sure to wear flowers in your hair)." My two favorite thoughts... California and Anne.

The song called my name. California! I could hardly wait. Love everywhere, the Golden Gate Park, Haight-Ashbury, hippies... *freedom!* But first I had to survive Ocean City.

After a session of heart-stirring music, the musicians packed up their instruments. I got the nerve and shuffled over. "You guys were great. Which one's Tim?"

A guitar player in a tie-dye shirt with long wavy black hair answered, "That's me, man."

"I really loved the music. Thanks a lot. My friend Anne told me to stop by. She said you'd be great and she was right. Have you seen her?"

"No. I expected her. She promised she was going to sing a few tunes. She's always here. She has an amazing voice. Man, I hope she's okay," Tim said. "I'm worried."

"Oh yeah, why's that?" I asked.

"I had a feeling when she told me her old boyfriend was coming to town he'd hassle her. She was so bummed. She didn't want to see him."

Ocean City, NJ. Enjoying the view on the boardwalk.
Photo credit: Jack Freeman - Longport, NJ

12 | Good Times, Bad Times

I walked out of the pavilion onto the packed boardwalk. I gazed across the faceless crowd that moved like ripples... People everywhere, yet no one to talk to... and no Anne. I'd never seen so many people.

The aroma of funnel cake teased my shrunken stomach. Friends and families celebrated life together, vacationing, enjoying, loving...

I stood without a single friend. Homeless, isolated, desolate.

The Shriver's sign glowed above the crowd as the evening shade inched across the wooden walkway. The sun faded toward the horizon behind the expansive row of shops across the way.

The ocean flowed behind me. I bounced on my toes and kept looking for Anne. I could see bald heads, hair in buns, braided hair, but none with flowers. Among the throngs of thousands it would be a miracle to find her.

Vacationers poured up and down and in and out of the shops, arcades, and eateries. Cheerful families and friends were everywhere, laughing, smiling, and eating ice cream.

What would it be like to have a happy family? What would it be like to take a family vacation? What would it be like to be able to afford a vacation? What would it be like not to live in constant fear?

Everyone had someone... except me. I stood by myself, endless miles from home.

Home? I wondered what Mom was doing. *How about Judy? Fritz? Eric? Keith? Davo? The twins? My friends at the park?*

In Ocean City, I was a stranger to everyone and everything. With no place to stay, freedom wasn't feeling so free. I longed for a familiar face. I longed for Anne.

How could I have been so stupid to trust John? I knew nothing about this town. Everything cast more doubt on my decision to escape. But then there was California... waiting with peace, love, and flower power!

My isolation and solitude intensified. Would I get caught by the cops? Every time one walked by, I did my best to blend in.

My shoulders drooped. I ran my fingers through my hair and pushed the bangs out of my eyes. The darker it got outside, the darker my inner thoughts became.

I rubbed my palms together, overwhelmed with uneasiness and self-doubt. I questioned my sanity... but it was too late. My mind had overloaded. No answers and too many questions.

I took a break from the commotion on the boardwalk and made my way back through the pavilion. A guitar player was strumming "Yesterday," as if to remind me when all my troubles were far away.

I stared across the blackening endless ocean. The night sky worked its way closer, filling my head with bleak reminders. I was homeless. There was no place to hide. And the cops were everywhere.

Waves crashed over the empty beach. Mist sprayed across my forehead. My thoughts intertwined with fear and paranoia. I fixated on my desperation... *Where will I stay? How will I survive?*

Out of the corner of my eye, I saw a shadow move in my direction. A male voice broke my daze. "Pretty far-out, isn't it?"

"Oh yeah, it's amazing," I said.

A tall guy with shoulder-length brown hair stood to my right. He looked to be about nineteen or so. "Hi, I'm Mark."

We talked about so many things. He hitchhiked, too. We shared stories about our love for Rock 'n' Roll, and girls, of course. We connected in no time.

"I'm only here until the end of the summer," he said. "Then I'm going to hitch out west. I really want to go to Haight-Ashbury."

"Wow, so do I!"

"Let's hitch out there together," he said.

"Far-out!"

I opened up. Having someone to talk to was a godsend. Despite the small talk, I was riddled with angst about finding shelter for the night.

"Where are you staying here?" I asked.

"I don't really have a place. I don't have any money and I haven't been here long enough," Mark shared. "I've just been asking girls if I can crash at their pads."

"How do you do that?"

"Watch." Mark went up to a couple of pretty girls walking on the boardwalk. "Can we crash at your pad?"

They giggled and kept walking.

Mark turned to me and shrugged. "We gotta just keep on trying."

He was enjoying the game of this, but walking up to strange girls would be scary for me. I was too shy. I couldn't believe Mark was so comfortable doing it. He was a natural. But I also couldn't think of any other option.

How could he just walk up to strangers? Pretty strangers, no less?

It wasn't a pickup line, it was our desperate attempt to find a place to stay. Time ticked away. Our options dwindled. Cold harsh reality pressed out every thought other than dread.

I let Mark do the talking. I stayed in the background and did my best to fade away. Meanwhile I was on high alert for cops. Every time I spotted one, I would sneak into the crowd and try to blend like a chameleon.

After the coast cleared I'd go back to the search. Each time we'd see a couple of cute girls, Mark would go up and ask our standard refrain, "Can we crash at your pad?"

Some girls grinned... some ignored us... others stopped and flirted and then went on their way.

It was going from bad to worse!

49

13 | Help!

Mark continued to talk to the girls we met on the boardwalk.

The evening passed and our luck changed. A couple of girls said, "Sure. We're here with our parents but you can stay on our porch."

The weight of the universe lifted from my shoulders. *Yeah!*

"Thank you!" Even a hard porch would be a welcome relief.

And that was how our housing arrangements went for the next couple of days. A porch from late night until the early sweltering July sun came up, then we'd walk around town and on the boardwalk until eight o'clock when the beach opened. After that, we'd take a nap, search for a job, and hang out at Shriver's Pavilion.

Mark became the big brother I never had. He was my hero. I looked forward to heading out to San Francisco with him at the end of the summer.

Every evening wrapped with panic and weariness until we found a place to keep our bodies for the night. Every day was spent in fear of running out of money and food. The terror of starving hovered in the back of my mind... always. And every moment was clouded by the dread of getting busted.

One afternoon, after searching for jobs in town, I was supposed to meet Mark at three o'clock at Shriver's Pavilion. He was late so I sat on one of the benches. My empty stomach reminded me how hungry I was.

A round bald-headed guy sat next to me and set down a pizza box beside himself.

I smiled. "Hello."

He grunted back and opened the box, struggling to pull a cheesy slice of pizza away from the rest, then shoved the pointed part into his mouth and devoured it in no time. Then another and another... The smell was driving me nuts.

Mark finally showed up. "I'm practically broke. I never realized money would go so fast," he confessed. "This place is expensive. We gotta get jobs."

I nodded my agreement.

"But..." Mark added, "I've got some great news, man. I met these cool chicks here the other day. They're cousins. I just ran into them again and they're gonna let me crash on their porch tonight," he said. "They'll be stopping by a little later. You'll like them. I have my eyes on Jill." Mark grinned.

Standing across from Shriver's Candy Store, the sweet aroma of taffy tempted my taste buds... an ever-present reminder of my limited and dwindling food supply.

My cop paranoia continued. Every time I spotted someone in uniform I prayed I wouldn't be busted.

Later in the evening two smiling girls wandered over. "This is Jill and this is Maggie," Mark introduced them.

Jill was a brunette with crazy frizzy hair sticking out all over the place. Maggie was brunette too, but her hair was long and straight, held down by a red tie-dye headband. They looked to be older, around eighteen or so.

After awkward introductions, the four of us ambled around the boardwalk.

After a while, Mark leaned over and said something to Maggie.

She then came over and walked next to me. "Mark tells me you need a place to stay tonight, too."

"I sure do."

"You're welcome to crash on our back porch with him."

"Thank you."

"But you have to be gone by the time my parents get up in the morning. My dad can be nasty."

"Okay. Thanks a million." *Nasty? Like call-the-cops nasty?*

Photo by author. Ocean City, NJ boardwalk.

My paranoia was always there but faded into the background while we smiled, laughed, and flirted, basking in the comfort of newfound friends.

The four of us shuffled through the crowd. Mark worked his charm on Jill. Her doe-eyed stare made it obvious that she reciprocated.

In the meantime, Maggie and I found our fair share of things to talk and crack-up about. At age fifteen, I was intrigued by her older hippie worldliness.

Music was one of the bonds we shared. We chatted about the beautiful lyrics of the Beatles and Moody Blues to Crosby, Stills, Nash & Young, through the psychedelic sounds of Hendrix, Pink Floyd, and Uriah Heep.

We waltzed in and out of the crowd and wove our way back to the pavilion, where the musicians broke into the song, "With a Little Help from My Friends," and the crowd joined in.

We sat together on one of the benches with our backs to the ocean. The music and laughter lifted my spirits.

Mark and I shared our dream of going to California.

"You'll love it out there," Jill chimed in. "It's so happening. I spent some time there last summer. Haight-Ashbury is where it's at!"

I could hardly wait.

Then our topics got more serious. We discussed politics, the older generation, and the Vietnam war.

At that point Maggie's expression intensified. Tears leaked from the corners of her eyes. "My boyfriend is in the Army. I hope they don't send him off to Vietnam. I don't want my Todd to kill... or get killed."

Her face blazed red as she continued. "I hate that damn war. I hate all war. Isn't it a sin to kill?" She looked past me and out onto the rolling ocean. Her tears glistened in the dim light.

I had no idea what to do. I bowed my head and searched for words that never came. We sat in silence.

Through her tears she sobbed. "I'm sorry. War sucks. I hate it. It just doesn't make any sense. Why can't we all live in harmony?"

"You're right," I said, trying to comfort her. "Why can't everyone live in harmony?"

She looked at me with a sad smile that lifted the corners of her mouth. "Love is the answer," she said, sniffing back a tear.

At around ten o'clock, Ocean City started packing it in for the night, and we followed suit. Jill, Mark, Maggie, and I left Shriver's. We walked the frenzied boardwalk and down the ramp into the stillness of the sleepy vacation town, up to 3rd Street.

Used with permission. william87/Depositphotos.com

When we reached the girls' house, it was dark and quiet with only one light on. We snuck through the tight space between the cottages. The four of us sat on aluminum slatted lawn chairs at the back of the yard. The plastic straps were a luxury compared to the hard benches I had grown accustomed to.

We did our best to be quiet but our outbursts of laughter and giddiness were hard to control. The words rolled off our lips. We talked about Woodstock, San Francisco, and our lives. Then the conversation became more serious. Maggie shared that her mother had cancer. I talked about my dad's drinking and my running away.

Jill changed the subject. "Let's talk about our favorite bands. I love the Fab Four. I'd have to say my favorite song is 'Strawberry Fields Forever.' I'd love to live there... forever."

Maggie said, "I love anything by Crosby, Stills, Nash & Young. I saw them at Woodstock last summer, and they were fabulous. The whole concert was far-out. I love the song they sang about it called, 'Woodstock.' A great tune with cool memories."

Mark shared his love for the San Francisco sound… The Dead, Big Brother, Quicksilver, and especially the Airplane. "My favorite tune of theirs is 'Somebody to Love'. Besides, I'm in love with Grace Slick."

"Isn't everybody?" I chimed in.

The gang laughed.

After our hysteria, Mark got back on track. "I can't wait to get out there. Maybe we can meet Grace Slick. She lives right there in Haight-Ashbury. It would be so cool."

"I agree," I answered. "I can't wait either. I love all those bands, but the Stones do my favorite song." Ever since I could remember, life was a constant struggle to find shelter, especially at home. "Gimme Shelter" was my perfect battle cry.

Mark and I carried on about everything Rock 'n' Roll… the Yardbirds, Zeppelin, the Stones, Pink Floyd… *Rolling Stone* magazine… all magic!

While we rambled about music, the girls drifted into their own gossip session, huddled in secret. I overheard Jill whisper, "Did you hear what happened to Anne?"

My ears perked up. I half listened to Mark while I caught bits and pieces of Jill and Maggie's muffled conversation. Their voices were faint. "Anne" … "in trouble" … "boyfriend" … "jerk" … "gone for the summer"… was about all I heard.

Then Jill jumped up. "Man, it's 2:00 A.M. already. We've got to get to bed. Good night."

Mark and I crept onto the porch, careful with every move. "Good night," I said quietly. "Thanks again."

At least I had a place to park my body for the night without looking over my shoulder for a cop to appear. Maggie's father was another story.

I kept reminding myself that sleeping on the wooden porch was like the Ritz compared to being cramped into the back seat of Eric's Corvair that first night. I didn't sleep much though. Mark snored like a roaring jet engine. I trembled at the thought of Maggie's parents finding us. My body froze but my mind bounced all over the place.

Had they been talking about "my" Anne? *Gone? Would Maggie's parents hear Mark snoring? What if the door opened? Should I grab Mark and run? What if they called the cops?*

The sun rose bright and hot and early in Ocean City on those July mornings. Mark and I snuck away at 5:15. I must have dozed off and gotten some sleep because I felt refreshed and ready to start a new day.

Of course, Anne was the first thing on my mind. I sure hoped I would see her. We plodded through the sleepy streets of Ocean City. It was much too early for Mark. He was only half awake. I'd have to wait to ask him about Anne.

Among my cluttered thoughts, I realized that if I was back home right now, I'd be lugging around a sack, delivering newspapers with my brothers and one of my sisters. *How were they? Was my route getting delivered? How was Mom? Man, I missed them. Did they miss me?*

I wanted to run. I wanted to be back home. I wanted to be in the kitchen with Fritz, Judy, Eric, and Keith eating a delicious bowl of Quisp cereal. My stomach twisted.

But then the thought of Dad's rage charged back into my brain, and escape became my reality... Ocean City, and Anne, and Mark, and the girls, and finding a job, and surviving.

Mark and I made our way to Shriver's Pavilion in our morning silence. When we got there, we perched on our favorite bench and watched the boardwalk. Walkers and bikers appeared, first a few here and a few there, then more and more. Ocean City came alive.

Mark came alive, too.

The world woke up and we were there in the thick of it, breathing in the sunshine and salt. The seagulls chattered, the ocean churned, bike wheels rattled across the boards... *Thump, thump... Thump, thump... Thump, thump...*

The faint smell of bacon sizzled through the morning breeze and tempted my watering tastebuds, sending a message of hunger to my stomach.

Mark and I sat alone. I pulled out the dwindling loaf of bread. "Want a peanut butter sandwich?"

"Yeah, it's not bacon, but that would hit the spot," he replied.

We sat in silence, munching our sandwiches and watching people stroll by. I wrestled with my thoughts. Was now the right time to ask Mark? I wanted to know about Anne but I dreaded his answer...

Photo by author. Ocean City, NJ boardwalk.

My morning job hunting didn't go well. Disappointment after disappointment... the more rejections, the more hopeless and dire reality became. I tried to tuck away painful memories and remember that I was where I wanted to be.

Along the way, and with every step, I also looked for Anne.

After a morning of harsh rejections, I walked back to the pavilion on high alert. My head turned with every blonde who walked by.

When I got to Shriver's there were a few dozen people scattered around talking and listening to a guitar player.

But no Anne.

Minutes later, Mark stood by my side. From his frown I could tell he hadn't had any better luck than me.

Defeated, he said, "If we want to find jobs, I think we need to leave Ocean City."

No! We can't leave. Shriver's was already my home away from home. And what about Anne? If we left, my chances of seeing her again would vanish.

I looked at Mark. He stared back at me like he was peering into my soul. My muscles tensed. My eyes watered. "We'll come back here at the end of the day. We just need to find work." He paused. Then he threatened, "We can always panhandle if you don't want to leave! But man, we have to do something. I only have a dollar left in my pocket."

"Panhandle!" *How could I possibly ask strangers for spare change?* The thought made me shudder. My dread intensified. We had to live!

15 | World in Changes

Mark and I sat on the bench and finished the last of our peanut butter and bread. *What now? No more food. Little money. Little hope.*

I leaned forward and tried to make sense of Mark's money-making ideas. I didn't want to beg but I sure didn't want to leave Ocean City either.

"Where do you want to go?" My voice choked.

"How about Cape May or Stone Harbor? They're just down the road." His voice was hopeful.

"If we're gonna go, let's get going, so we can get back and hang out with Jill and Maggie tonight... and maybe see Anne if we're lucky." I clasped my hands in a prayer gesture.

"You're pathetic," Mark said.

My heart lifted when I heard a cheery familiar voice. "Heeeeey Larry, how's it going?" It was Joe and Eric walking toward us! Like a cat that swallowed a bird, their faces beamed.

I jumped to my feet. "Hey! Whatcha been up to?"

"Enjoying this view. Sure is beautiful here." Joe jerked his head to watch a gorgeous girl stroll by.

Eric chimed in, "Yeah, and the ocean's nice, too."

"Speaking of the view, I met this amazing flower girl and I'm in love," I said, hugging myself. Eric and Joe looked at Mark standing next to me. "Sorry, this is Mark."

We all gave each other the overhand hippie handshake.

"You find a job yet?" Eric asked.

"No. I'm bummed. We're hitching to Cape May this afternoon. Maybe we can find something there."

Eric said, "We're going to Cape May tomorrow. Why don't you come with us?"

I looked to Mark. He smiled. "That would be great. Thanks, man!"

Joe said, "Today, let's do some sightseeing." A beautiful girl walked past. "Hey Chiquita, I think I love you," became our new girl-crazy teen motto.

We took the afternoon off and walked the boardwalk, laid on the beach, and hung around at Shriver's. Joe, Eric, and Mark competed to find the prettiest girls, but none compared to my Anne. Every glimpse of blonde seeded my heart with hope. But that hope shriveled and died each and every time.

We found our place on the beach among the throngs of vacationers. The four of us told stories, laughed, and did our best to take in every ounce of scenery. It didn't take long before the sun baked us.

"Let's take a dip," I said. The sand scorched my toes as I ran toward the water.

On the ocean's edge, heavy muck and foamy swell blanketed my feet. The bottom of my pants got soaked and stuck to my skin, weighing my legs down. I plunged head-first into the surf. The salty Atlantic washed over my body and refreshed my spirit with her holy water.

We splashed, teased, and clowned... lost in the freedom of the moment. A swim was the refreshment I needed.

When we got out, we slogged back to our designated perching spot to continue our girl-watching adventures. The glaring sun sucked the energy from my weary body. I laid on my stomach, roasted, and drifted off into oblivion.

Time evaporated into late afternoon. The waves of the sea competed with the waves of people on the boardwalk heading back to their temporary homes to prepare for evening fun... moms with kids on both hips and fathers carrying umbrellas, chairs, and blankets. I yearned to be with them. I imagined being a part of their family, laying on the beach, swimming, and when exhausted, going out for dinner.

I packed up my paper bag pillow and T-shirt blanket and joined my friends as we moved off the beach. When we reached the boardwalk, the smell of greasy delicious French fries made our bellies ache with hunger.

Eric looked up and said, "Man, I could sure use some fries. How 'bout you?"

"Far-out!"

Once again Eric came through. He got in line while Joe, Mark, and I waited at the pavilion.

Eric came back with enough fries to feed an army. I paused just long enough to say, "Thanks, man!"

We devoured the delicious banquet in no time. Our stomachs filled like the crowd on the boardwalk. We took every opportunity to appreciate the view with our familiar refrain, "Hey Chiquita, I think I love you!"

Still, I daydreamed about Anne. I was a goner, lost in the movies I created in my thoughts. *Where is she? Will I ever see her again? Is she okay?*

The throngs moved across the boardwalk and groups of familiar faces and new friends moved in and out of the pavilion... smiling, winking, and flashing the peace sign.

Jill and Maggie bounced in, excited to share their day. After brief introductions, Jill blurted, "We went down to Wildwood today. It was *so* cool. They have some far-out amusement parks. What a blast!"

Maggie added, "The beaches were huge. But man, there wasn't anything like Shriver's."

Time passed quickly. One moment I pumped with life... the ocean, the boardwalk, friends... The next I pumped with puppy love. *No Anne.* I kept hoping to see her head pop out of the crowd, yelling my name.

A moment later still, I pumped with paranoia... the nagging dread of getting busted. And more often than I thought, I'd spot someone who looked like my brother Fritz, or sister Jude, or Mom. *How are they?* I wanted to reach out and call but I knew if I talked to Mom, I'd lose it. Plus the thought of Dad possibly answering brought sheer anguish.

Eric looked at his watch. "We've got to get back to our motel. My parents are calling at eight o'clock."

"See you tomorrow," Joe said. He pointed across the boardwalk to the end of 9th Street. "We'll meet you right over there at eleven."

I flashed him the peace sign and yelled, "Thanks, man. Good night."

Eric and Joe headed for their motel while Jill, Maggie, Mark, and I shared the rest of the evening and hung around the pavilion. Eventually we wandered out onto the boardwalk, enjoying the night.

We ended the evening on lawn chairs behind the girls' vacation cottage, until it was time to camp out on the back porch.

Maggie said, "Hey man, Mom wants us to go back home with her for a few days next week."

Mark sat up. "Bummer."

Maggie continued, "It's cool, man. We'll be back but you've gotta find another place to crash until we do. Dad's staying. I wouldn't sleep here if I were you. He'll catch you for sure."

Fear rushed through my veins. That could happen any time. He could catch us. Scary... but worse, in a few days we'd be even more homeless. Back on our own.

"Good night. Remember to be outta here early. Dad's been asking too many questions," Maggie warned and then they snuck inside.

Once again Mark and I hid. Once again we slept in terror. Once again Mark snored.

What's that? The sun was peeking over the horizon when a light came on inside the cottage. Plates banged, cabinet doors slammed, there was a male grumbling. I panicked.

16 | We Gotta Get
Out of This Place

I got up my courage and whispered, "Mark. Hey, Mark." No answer came, just ear-piercing snoring. I moved as slowly and quietly as I could. I shook him by the shoulder. "Hey, man. We've gotta get out of here."

He stopped snoring and looked up.

"We've gotta go now."

The light went out inside. He and I waited a few minutes for the coast to clear, then we vamoosed.

We passed the early morning hours wandering the streets of our vacation homeless home. When we got to the boardwalk, the smell of eggs and bacon was overpowering. We had to break Mark's last dollar. We got two doughnuts each and made our way to Shriver's.

The two of us sat on our now familiar bench and savored our breakfast delicacies. Things were getting desperate. We were down to our last few coins. We were surely in trouble. We both needed to find jobs or resort to panhandling. What could be worse? I swallowed hard.

Mark and I walked up and down looking in the shop windows, while not passing up the opportunity to drink in the passing scenery.

"I sure hope Cape May is this cool." Mark gave a thumbs up.

"Well, Anne won't be there."

"You are freaking hopeless, man. Besides, she ain't here either," Mark reminded me.

We wrapped up our morning adventures and walked down the ramp to the end of 9th Street. In a few minutes, the familiar Corvair pulled up and Eric and Joe whisked us south.

They were filled with excitement and high spirits, as was always the case. We joked, laughed, and goofed off the whole way there. It took us forty minutes... a long way to try to hitch every day to get to a job.

A few minutes before we arrived, we passed the Wildwood exit. Mark pointed to the sign. "Maggie and Jill were here yesterday. They loved it. Maybe we can check it out later?"

"Sure. That's cool," Eric said.

In an abrupt transition, like flipping a switch, the fast and furious Garden State Parkway poured right into a quaint street at the entrance to Cape May. We headed east toward the ocean and boardwalk.

It was a different world. Nothing like Ocean City. The streets looked like a backdrop to a movie. There was no "board" walk, just a paved sidewalk and very few shops. No excitement here, especially for four teenaged boys. Where was the beach? Where were the bikinis?

I checked out the shops. "Man, there's no way we're gonna find a job here."

Cape May Convention Hall. Photo Credit: Jack Freeman – Longport, NJ

"Bummer, man. This sure ain't where it's at." Mark wasn't too optimistic, and neither was I.

He pointed to a couple of the countless white-haired tourists. "This town isn't for us. Would we really want to work here? What was I thinking? Let's get out of here."

Music to my ears. "Yeah, let's go." I nodded. "Besides, who wants to hitch this far every day?"

"Let's check out Wildwood," Eric chimed in.

"Oh yeah!" Joe agreed. "I miss the chicks already."

We laughed the whole way to the car and back up the Garden State Parkway to our next hope... Wildwood, just fifteen minutes away. That was still a long hitch from Ocean City, but at least the name was cool... *Wild!*

Wildwood was happening. The boardwalk bustled with action, action, action, like a trippy carnival. Games, side-shows, and amusement parks... a glitzy wonderland... *Bang, bang, bang... pop, pop, pop... swoosh, swoosh, swoosh...* An endless smorgasbord of sounds competed.

We saw 'help wanted' signs here and there. The aroma of pizza, burgers, and fries tempted my rapidly emptying stomach.

It was all too much until Joe treated us to pizza and a soda. We sat on a bench, enjoyed our cheesy feast, and partook of our favorite activity... appreciating the swimsuit-clad beauties.

Ahhh... contentment... Yet I was haunted by the lingering awareness that Eric and Joe would soon be leaving and their kindness and generosity would have to end.

Wildwood was happening, but it just wasn't Ocean City. There was no Shriver's... no home base... and no Anne... and no Jill for Mark. Plus it was too far to hitchhike. There was no way we wanted to leave our homeless home in Ocean City... at least not until the end of summer when we'd be San Francisco bound.

I breathed a sigh of relief when Mark said, "I don't want to work here. It's just too far."

"I agree, man." So we took the rest of the afternoon and marveled at the sights, sounds, and tasty scents of Wildwood.

On the long cramped drive back to Ocean City, Eric, Joe, and Mark talked away while I sat in silence. Reality settled in. Eric and Joe—the guys who'd rescued me back on the turnpike—were leaving. Leaving for good. Heavy salted air filled my lungs and blasted through my hair.

Those two had been godsends and they would soon be gone forever. Thank heavens I had Mark.

By the time we got back to Ocean City, it was after seven o'clock. Eric and Joe pulled up to the dead end of 9th Street at the boardwalk and we all got out.

Eric left his Corvair running. "Man, we've really got to get going. My parents are going to kill me. I was supposed to have the car home by dinner time."

"Well, goodbye. Thanks for everything." My spirit sank. We gave each other the hippie handshake.

Joe put his hand on my shoulder. "Hang in there, man. Be safe."

"Need some money to tide you over?" Eric asked, reaching into his pocket. He pulled out a few coins. "Wow, this is all I've got left. Man, I need to buy gas."

Without prompting, Joe did the same. All he had was a one-dollar bill and some loose change.

In his most casual tone, Mark said, "It's cool. But thank you anyway."

I freaked out inside. *Cool! Cool? We're practically broke. No income. No place to stay. But cool!*

I certainly didn't expect Eric and Joe to do as much as they had and I never expected a handout... but *"Cool?"* Yikes!

I fought hard to hold back my tears. "Goodbye. Thanks again." My right hand held up the sign of peace.

There they went—my connection to Pennsylvania. Two of the greatest friends in my life that I would never see again. They hopped into my former bunkhouse, turned around, and headed west.

Eric's peace sign waved out the left window and Joe's out the right. I watched their car disappear... forever! My heart plunged. My arms dropped. I stood silent.

"I'm starving," Mark announced, breaking me out of my trance.

We put our change together. I knew it would be our last money without having to beg. Even if we found jobs, we probably wouldn't get paid for a couple of weeks.

We walked to the grocery store to see what our few coins could buy for dinner. I thought long-term... another loaf of bread and a large box of Jujyfruits candy. Mark grabbed a container of potato salad.

Back at Shriver's, there was still no Anne. Mark taught me about a new gourmet delight... potato salad sandwiches! With our stomachs full, we walked the boardwalk. I kept my eyes peeled for a certain flower girl.

The more time I spent with Mark, the more of a big brother he became. He didn't have a shy cell in his body. We made a lot of friends everywhere we went.

As we walked past 7th Street, we heard a familiar voice. "Hi, guys!" Jill and Maggie waved.

"How'd the job search go?" Maggie asked.

Mark and I looked at each other and got into another fit of laughter. It was contagious and the girls laughed, too, even though they didn't know what was so funny.

We spent the rest of the evening hanging out with them and walking the boardwalk... the whole time half paying attention... and half looking for Anne.

Should I ask them? I didn't want them to think I was eavesdropping... Then, I spotted a dime on one of the planks. Was that a sign? Should I call Mom?

17 | You Can't Always Get What You Want

When I reached to pick up the dime, my eyes were drawn to a bright green sign in the window of an ice cream shop with bold black letters. "Help Wanted."

"Look," I pointed to the notice in the window.

"Go for it," Mark said.

Jill and Maggie cheered me on.

The second I pushed open the glass door, a bell tinkled. I bumped into a ponytailed guy mopping the floor who stopped and looked at me.

"I saw the 'help wanted' sign. Are they still looking?"

"Yeah," he said.

"May I please speak with the boss?" I asked.

"Mr. Peters is gone for the day. But he gets here at 9:00 tomorrow."

"That's great. I'll be back first thing," I said. I headed out then turned back. "Thank you." I flashed him the peace sign.

He returned the same. "Don't take any chances. Be here at 9:00. Good luck."

Nine o'clock couldn't come soon enough.

Jill, Maggie, and Mark pumped me with encouragement all the way to their house. I couldn't stop talking about my big opportunity! But in the back of my mind... dread. *What if the position was already filled? What if he asked my age? What if... what if... what if...?*

Finally, maybe things were looking up.

The four of us whispered stories in the backyard. Our outbursts of laughter were hard to muffle. Like always, we had a blast and lost track of time.

Mark yawned. "Let's get some sleep."

"Good night." The girls went inside.

Mark and I took our places on the porch. After a long day we were dead tired. In less than a minute I could hear his soft snores.

I faded away dreaming of the possibility that the next day would be the start of a new life... and maybe I'd even see Anne.

The next morning, we snuck away as the edges of light peered over the horizon and plodded along in our morning stupor. We got to the boardwalk in time to watch the fiery red edge of the ocean wake as the sun popped its rays over the sea and greeted us. My spirit brightened with the sky.

We walked our now familiar pathway up and down the boardwalk, breathing in the heavy salt air, drinking in the golden sunlight, watching the yawning town wake. The breakfast spots rolled up their metal gates here and there and welcomed vacationers.

Mark and I passed an empty Shriver's, sat on the beach, and enjoyed the calming ocean waves. We munched on our bread and Jujyfruits.

"It's 8:30," Mark reminded me. "Better get to the ice cream shop before he hires someone else."

"Already?" I blurted as I took the last bite of bread. I stood up fast and wiped the crumbs from the corners of my mouth and used my fingers to comb through my hair so I wouldn't look pathetic. "Wish me luck!"

I found a bench across from Mr. Peters' store, fidgeting on the edge of the seat. When he arrived, I watched him unlock the shop. Like a jack-in-the-box, I jumped up and shot across the boardwalk. I wanted to run but my mind told me I shouldn't look desperate.

Mr. Peters turned around and said, "Good morning, can I help you?"

"Yes, sir. I saw the 'help wanted' sign and wanted to ask about the job."

"I'm impressed. You're here early. That's great. Do you have any experience working in an ice cream shop?"

"Um... no. But I can learn."

"I like that," Mr. Peters said. He showed me around a little and said, "Be here tomorrow at four o'clock."

"Thank you, sir," I said.

"Call me Pete. See you tomorrow."

I could hardly keep my feet on the ground. I wanted to jump up and cheer! I dashed back to Mark to share the good news.

"Far-out!" Mark said. "I hope your luck rubs off on me. I'm off. See you here at lunchtime."

The bench was warm. People watching had become my way to pass the time, and of course it gave me a chance to maybe see... you know who.

I couldn't wait to share the news with Jill and Maggie... and if my luck held out, Anne. But there was one person I really needed to share the good news with... Mom.

I went in search of a phone. My insides vibrated. I was overwhelmed with excitement, and of course, trembling with fear.

The phone booth was at the end of 9th Street. My fingers peeled the dime from my clammy palm and my hand shook as I slid it into the slot. I turned the dial from zero slowly to the end. The dial released and returned to its resting spot. The phone clicked and my dime dropped back into the coin return when the operator answered.

"May I please make a collect call to..." I rattled off the number.

Ring...

Used with permission. jetcityimage2/Depositphotos.com

Ring... The second ring was deafening.

I clutched the receiver, my legs felt like noodles, and my mind blanked. My insides were tearing apart with turmoil.

Ring...

I trembled as I attempted to put the receiver back. I fumbled to find the hook. I hung up and dug my dime out of the coin return.

Tears streamed down my face. So close, yet held back by panic. The temptation to pick up the phone again was intense. I wanted to share my good news with Mom like I always did. I wanted to let her know I was okay. I wanted to let her know I would send money as soon as I could.

But my fear was stronger. My doubts were endless...

What if Dad answered? What if Mom started crying? Besides, it would cost a fortune to accept the phone charges. We didn't have that kind of money.

I struggled over what to do... so I did nothing. It was almost lunch time. Mark would be at the pavilion soon. Our bench was full so I sat on the edge of another. Next to me was a mother pushing a stroller back and forth to lull her baby to sleep. It was hypnotic, but not enough that I couldn't turn my head when a blonde girl walked by... still hoping to find Anne.

"How was the rest of your morning?" Mark asked when he arrived.

I pulled myself up off the bench and took a few steps away because I didn't want to wake the baby. "I just called home. But I hung up before anyone could answer."

"Are you kidding? Cheer up. There's always tomorrow," Mark said. What a comforting big brother. He slapped me on the back. "Besides, today's not all bad. You're my good luck charm. I found a job, too."

I couldn't embrace his good news. It didn't lighten the disappointment I had in myself. I continued to replay my failure.

I gave a slight smile and pulled the Jujyfruits out of my pocket. Flipping one into my mouth, I handed the box to Mark.

I stretched the tension out of my muscles. We shuffled to the edge of the pavilion. Looking down the boardwalk, my eyes widened. My heart pounded. I couldn't believe what I saw.

Coming in my direction were Jill, Maggie, a tall guy with a short Army-style haircut... and Anne!

She paused when she saw me. I stood like a statue. *Was that her boyfriend?*

Photo by author. Ocean City, NJ boardwalk.

18 | What a Day for a Daydream

Then Anne shined the biggest smile. *She must have worked things out with him.* I sighed. A fake smile was all I could muster. The closer they got, I could see the Army guy's hand clutching another.

It wasn't Anne's... it was Maggie's!

My emotions see-sawed. My smile became real. Relief spilled over as they approached. "Hi!" I said with a shaky laugh.

"Hi, to you. Sorry I haven't been around," Anne said.

She left the group and stood next to me. I could feel the heat and presence of her body. Our arms touched. At that moment I would have given her the world. It didn't matter that I hadn't seen her. Nothing mattered anymore. She was here... with me... warm and loving.

Maggie interrupted. "Larry, this is my sweetheart, Todd. He's home from the Army for a few days." She threw her arms around him.

Jill asked, "Where's Mark?"

Feeling the heat from Anne, I stuttered and pointed behind me. "He's over there."

Jill hurried over.

Anne grabbed my arm. "Walk with me," she said as she pulled me to the railing.

All of a sudden, like a dream... there we were, just us, in a bubble of our own. Anne wrapped her arm around the rail as if she needed support. She turned to face me.

I melted as I looked into her eyes. Those sapphire blues became cloudy. "I had a bad couple of days," she said. "My boyfriend from last summer wanted to get back together. What a jerk. We had a horrible break-up. I was in the kitchen and he saw my diary on the coffee table. And... he read it," her voice cracked. "I was so mad. How could he invade my private thoughts? I pushed him out the door and told him I didn't want to see him again."

I kept staring at Anne, so glad to have her back with me.

"Summer was over and he had to leave for football practice anyway. He started flirting with some cheerleader named Ellen. Every time I saw him, they were together. Well, she doesn't want him, so now he's chasing me again. That jerk thought I'd cool off by now. He wouldn't stop calling. He even came and pounded on the door until Dad yelled at him to leave. I hid inside my room until I knew he left again for football camp," she continued to spill her story.

Without thinking, like a knight in shining armor, I reached for Anne's hand with both of mine. "You're safe with me. I won't let anything or anyone hurt you."

She looked up at me with a smile that expanded my heart.

We stood still. I absorbed her sweetness.

Mark broke the spell. "Hey, lovebirds! We're heading down the boardwalk. Come on!"

Embarrassed, I dropped her hand and chuckled. I didn't want the moment to end. "We'll catch up with you later," I yelled. Then I looked back into Anne's sparkling eyes. "Let's go walk on the beach."

We strolled for about ten minutes. My apprehensive teen mind struggled. Being shy, it was hard to know what to say, so I grabbed her hand which told her I wanted to be with her.

I guess she felt the same way, because she interlaced our fingers. Electric jolts burst through my body.

We meandered along at the edge of the ocean, feet sinking into the wet sand. The waves embraced our ankles and then let go.

"Look, Larry. Isn't this beautiful?" She bent over and held up a black seashell.

I looked at the treasure in her hand.

"It has a hole on top. If only I had a string or a chain, I could make you a necklace." She handed it to me. "I want you to have this. I think it might be magical."

My perpetual puppy love smile widened. "Thank you. It's the most far-out gift I've ever gotten."

I held it and wished on its magical charm. *May Anne fall as in love with me as I am with her. May this summer last forever.*

We walked and walked further south from beach to beach. 15th Street to 16th... on past 23rd Street. The boardwalk disappeared from our right. Time evaporated. I never wanted it to end.

We chatted endlessly. I shared my deepest secrets, my desires, my fears, and I yearned to hear more about her.

A gentle breeze blew through our hair and the rhythmic waves splashed our legs. I poured my heart and soul out about my father, my family, my fear of police, and my ultimate desire. "Mark and I are hitching out to Haight-Ashbury at the end of the summer."

Anne looked into my eyes. "Sounds like a cool place... but there are lots of other cool places."

"Like where?"

"Like here," she said, gently squeezing my wrist.

We flowed through relevant teenage topics and stories... deep to light-hearted... our fathers, families, the "generation gap," the war in Vietnam, the invasion of Cambodia, protests, the killing of students at Kent State, Flower Power, the Love Generation, Woodstock, concerts, John, Mark, Jill, Maggie, Shriver's...

But music was our magnet, filling in gaps and pauses, and Rock 'n' Roll was the thread that bonded us—The British Invasion, Acid Rock, and Folk.

We broke up the heavy stuff with a line or two from "Do You Believe in Magic," or "Yellow Submarine," or whatever crossed our minds... always ending in fits of uncontrollable laughter.

One beach ran into another. By the time our senses returned, it was late afternoon. We could have walked for hours more but time and reality hit, so we turned around and headed the miles back toward the pavilion.

We talked the whole way, my pulse hammering with every word and each step we took.

When we got back, our friends weren't there. A crowd was gathered in the corner singing with a guy strumming his guitar. Even though it was the music we both loved, I just wanted to be with Anne. Only Anne. My crush on her was intense. Nothing else mattered. I prayed she wouldn't stop to sing and break our trance.

"Hey, let's keep walking," Anne shouted over the singing crowd.

"That's music to my ears," I cheered. Being alone with Anne was all I wanted.

We continued our journey north to the other end of the boardwalk. On our way, the giant glowing Ferris wheel drew us in. Calypso music blared as the floating seats traveled skyward. All the rides were singing their own tunes.

"Oh, I love the merry-go-round," Anne said, pulling me toward the carousel. "When I was a little girl, I couldn't wait to get here and ride my very own pony. See that white one over there? That was my favorite. Oh man, Larry. Don't you just wish you could go back to those days?"

"They were fun, but nothing like today." I gave her an uneasy smile. "I sure wish I could afford to take you for a ride. What a dream."

"It doesn't matter. Someday maybe, but I don't care. You're my Knight in White Satin," she said as if she was giving away a secret.

My smile softened.

After wandering through the rides, we continued our walk up the boardwalk and over toward the sea and up the beach. We talked... and talked... and talked. We shared stories, our dreams, and we made summer plans.

Used with permission. iofoto/Depositphotos.com

"Hey, wanna dance?" Anne asked out of the blue.

There was no music, but I replied, "Sounds cool."

I took her in my arms and we danced to imaginary tunes. We spun in circles.

My dizziness took control and I pulled us both to the ground. We laid on the sand and howled.

When we stopped giggling, we sat knee to knee and pondered the depths of my fifteen-year-old questions and answers... peace and hope and love.

I lost track of time. I lost track of the hours. I lost track of everything that wasn't Anne.

Late night flowed into the wee hours. Millions of stars sparkled like diamonds. Mesmerized by the beauty of the spirit in the sky, we were the center of the universe. At first I didn't notice, but when Anne jumped up, I saw a set of headlights that made their way toward our stretch of private beach.

She tugged on my shirt. "We'd better get going. We've got to get off the beach." We squatted low and snuck off the sand.

Anne stepped fast. I followed. She stopped after a few blocks then turned around. "That's my house, the blue one," she said as she put a finger over her lips. "It's late, so we have to be quiet. We can't let my parents hear us."

The porch was two steps up so we tiptoed. "You sleep here," she whispered, pointing to the darkest corner. "But don't go near the window on the right. That's my parents' bedroom."

I followed her every word.

"You can use this chair cushion for a pillow and I'll hand you a blanket from my bedroom window," she said tilting her head to the one on the left.

"Thank you. Hey, I start my job at four o'clock tomorrow. I can't wait to get a paycheck so I can buy you an ice cream cone and take you on the merry-go-round."

"Wow! That will be great. But you don't have to buy me anything. Just be you," Anne replied.

"But you gave me the best gift ever." I pulled out the black seashell and held it toward her. She gently placed her head onto my shoulder. I wished time could stand still. I didn't want that moment to end.

"I've got to get going. I'll catch you at the window."

I got on my knees and squeezed into the two-foot space between her window and the metal porch swing glider. A light went on inside her room and Anne slowly lifted the window. She handed me a blanket. "Here. Sleep tight. But be sure to get out of here before my dad wakes up."

I grabbed the blanket. "Thank you. Sure, I'll be gone first thing. See you at Shriver's."

She leaned over and kissed me on the cheek.

In a daze, I watched as her window closed, then her beautiful face followed the shade, down and out of sight... a perfect vision to put my dreams into motion.

I made my makeshift bed and hid myself behind the glider as far from that window on the right as I could get. I faded into dreamland... my adorable Anne, laying on the other side of that window. Sweet euphoria!

Before I knew it, sun lit the morning sky. For the first endless moments I laid still, radar alert for any sound, and planned my careful escape.

I moved like a turtle, stood up, folded the blanket, turned around, and *bam,* I smashed into the glider. It screeched, squealed, and screamed in agony. Louder than any sound I ever heard.

Damn... I froze. Time froze. *How can I disappear?*

I held my breath, my feet rooted in place, suspended in eternity. The sound faded into the background of the waves and seagulls.

There was no movement inside. My feet unstuck themselves and I crept off the porch. The second I hit the pavement I took off, running a few houses inland. I didn't look back until I was safe. *Whew!*

Groggy from lack of sleep, I wandered the streets. The night replayed as I brushed my cheek where she'd planted that kiss. The warmth was still there, and lingered in my soul.

"What a day for a daydream!"

Anne, Anne, Anne. I couldn't wait to see her next. *I'm in love...*

I wove my way to the boardwalk, head in the clouds, ready for my fabulous day.

When I got there, the smell of pancakes filled the air. Sheer torture. My mouth watered. My stomach growled. My belly begged for what it couldn't have. The more I tried to ignore it, the hungrier I got. I looked for Mark but couldn't find him.

Shriver's was empty when I got there. The moment I sat on the bench, I tanked. I looked at my watch, 7:45—only fifteen minutes to safety when the beach would open.

I leaned back against the railing and nodded off and on. A few familiar faces trooped down to the beach on the steps to my left, then a couple more. For me it was still too early to tempt the authorities.

Sunny skies gave way to thick dark clouds. When the beach finally opened, a real nap called. Just as I got safely under the shelter of Shriver's Pavilion it started to sprinkle. I was surprised to find about fifteen or twenty people already sacked out under the boardwalk. I found an empty spot in the middle of the sleeping bodies.

"Under the Boardwalk" sang through my dreary head... and entwined itself with visions of Anne. I faded off, dreaming of spending the day together. At last, my weary body was parked in a safe legal place. No dads to worry about. No hassles. No cops. Sheer bliss.

No sooner had I dozed off than I felt a heavy tap-tap-tap on my left shoulder...

19 | Under the Boardwalk

Half awake, I peeked through one eye. Still dreaming about Anne, the silhouette of a large figure loomed over me. In a stern voice I heard, "Sergeant Richardson, Ocean City Detective Bureau."

Both of my eyes shot open. A man in a gray tweed sports coat with a buzz haircut stood over me. He whipped out his badge and flashed it in front of my face.

It took a few seconds to register. By the time I cleared the cobwebs from my head I realized there were two officers checking the IDs of all the people sleeping under the boardwalk.

I sat up at attention. Like always, my first instinct was to run... but there was no place to escape. I was trapped, just when my life was falling into place.

"How old are you, son?" Sergeant Richardson asked.

"Sixteen," I said, stretching the truth.

"Do your parents know where you are?"

"Yes," I answered. I thought there might have been a possibility.

"Okay. Don't go anywhere. We'll be right back."

The officers checked the IDs of everyone else. I must have been the only one under eighteen.

The officer came back and said, "Gather your things. You need to come with us."

Nowhere to run! Nowhere to hide!

The world closed around me. I trembled as I picked up my paper bag pillow. The officers escorted me up the steps, over the boardwalk, and down the other steps to the squad car waiting at the end of 9th Street.

Sergeant Richardson held the door open as I crawled into the back seat. Every pore in my body surged with intense panic.

As soon as the officers got into the front, I babbled my confession. "I'm only fifteen and my parents don't really know where I am."

They turned around, looked at me, and smiled. Their harshness melted away. Wow, maybe these guys weren't like the rest of the "establishment." They appeared human... even compassionate.

The five-minute drive to the police station seemed like an eternity. We pulled into the parking lot at around 8:30 that morning. All I wanted to do was run... but I was captured.

When we walked into the station, the secretary peered up at us. She continued to click away on her typewriter. Her glum frown added fuel to my distress.

They sat me on a hard wooden chair between two desks that overflowed with papers... my appropriate "hot seat."

They searched my precious brown paper bag and found a few smashed slices of bread, my spare clothes, a toothbrush, toothpaste, a bar of soap, and a seashell.

Used with permission. jirkaejc/Depositphotos.com

Sergeant Richardson said, "By the looks of that bread you must be hungry."

"Yes, sir," I blurted.

He turned to the typist and asked, "Mrs. Taylor, can you bring this young man breakfast?" After she left they pumped me with questions. "What are you doing in Ocean City?"

88

"I ran away. I was scared..."

"Scared? Of what?" he asked.

"My dad," I mumbled.

"Where are you from?"

"Pittsburgh."

"That's a long way from here. How did you get here?"

"I hitchhiked."

"Alone?"

"No, I started with a friend."

In a short time, Mrs. Taylor came in and handed me a plate of scrambled eggs and toast. My first cooked meal in days! I savored the delicacy of eggs and crunchy, buttery toast. It was some of the most delicious food I had ever tasted.

Then Sergeant Richardson sat behind the desk and picked up the phone. The dreaded moment came. "What's your number? We need to call your parents."

I scribbled it on a piece of paper and watched and waited as he dialed each digit. Each one was a step closer to my demise.

"Hello, Mrs. Schardt? This is Sergeant Richardson, Ocean City Detective Bureau. We have Larry here..."

They talked for a few minutes. The eggs weren't going down so easy anymore. He paused then handed me the phone. "Your mom wants to talk to you..."

I hesitated, took a deep breath, and clutched the phone. Fear, anticipation, home.

"Hi, Mom." I braced myself for the certain chewing out.

"You stinker."

What? No reprimand, no scolding, no anger... just love? That soft loving tone brought me back to the joy of being her child. It was the perfect Mom thing to say.

I failed to hold back the tears. Damn, this fifteen-year-old independent cowboy... broken!

I choked out, "I love you, Mom. I'm sorry... Please tell everyone else I love them, too." I handed the phone back to Sergeant Richardson. He continued his conversation with Mom.

The clicking typewriter stopped. Before I knew it, Mrs. Taylor came over and handed me a box of tissues. "It'll work out," she said. "Parents forget. You're a good kid."

The sergeant was still talking to Mom. I wiped the tears and listened.

"You can pick him up here. We're at the corner of 8th and Central Avenue. I'll be here 'til seven. Is that possible?"

Then I heard, "Really? Oh, sorry. What about your husband? ... Probably about a seven or eight-hour trip ... Okay, call me back and let me know if Mr. Schardt can do it. Thank you, Mrs. Schardt." He hung up.

The detective looked at me and said, "Your father might be coming to pick you up."

No! Nothing could be worse. I cringed, horrified. Dad would be furious. The room closed in around me. The air got thick and my breathing became heavy, making me feel light-headed. I couldn't run even if I wanted to. And besides, there was nowhere to go.

I trembled at the thought of Dad's temper... fueled by eight hours of intensified road rage...

I was doomed...

Used with permission. stokkete/Depositphotos.com

20 | Reflections of My Life

"My dad's picking me up?" My chest tightened.

Sergeant Richardson put the pen down. "Your mother said she wanted to come, but she wouldn't get home in time to get to work tonight... so she's sending your father."

My belly suddenly felt nauseous. Dad would be livid. I was sure he would still be in bed at that hour of the morning. Probably sleeping off a drunk. Would Mom be brave enough to wake him? Would he be sober? Would our old station wagon make the drive?

I squirmed in my seat. The only sound in the room was the clicking of the typewriter. With every minute that passed, the room got hotter and my stomach cramped.

Then the phone rang...

"Sergeant Richardson, it's Mrs. Schardt," Mrs. Taylor announced. "I'll transfer the call."

I watched his every move as he picked up the phone. He began scribbling on his notepad. "Yes, we can do that. Is one over eighteen?... No, no... That will be okay... So they'll pick him up by noon?... Larry will be here."

He hung up. With a half grin he said, "You're in luck, young man." He looked at his notepad. "Your neighbors, the Kemper brothers, are here in Ocean City on vacation and they're headed home today. Your mom arranged for them to pick you up at lunchtime. So it looks like you're going back to Pittsburgh... *today!*"

My fear subsided knowing my friends were coming to pick me up, and not my dad. Mom had come through once again. *How does she always do that? Whew!* Jim Kemper was eighteen, which made him old enough to sign for my custody. His brother Terry was a year older than me.

I had little time to think before the sergeant said, "Follow me."

He escorted me down a hall. As fast as the fear subsided it flooded back in. *Where was he taking me?*

The key ring rattled as he opened the first door, behind that was another one but this one had a small barred window.

Was I going to jail?

Sergeant Richardson pulled the cell door open, handed me a small green army blanket, and with a wave of his arm motioned for me to go inside. "Make yourself comfortable. We'll be back when your friends get here. Try to get some sleep."

I stared in disbelief as I watched the heavy steel door clang shut between us. Eerie silence screamed from the blank walls of solitude. I turned and scanned the room. I looked at a toilet without a seat, child-sized. There was a wooden bed. *Get comfortable on that?*

The only light filtered through two small windows cut out of the concrete walls. It was nothing like Otis's Mayberry cell... no pillow, no table, no lamp.

Overwhelmed with gloom, there was nothing to do but lay down. I unfolded the blanket, which wasn't long enough to even cover my legs. I closed my eyes. Thank heavens, I was only going to be in there for a few hours.

The thoughts rushed in. One after another, after another. Before I went home I needed to tell Mr. Peters I couldn't work at the ice cream store... I needed to see Anne... I needed to see Mark... I hoped the Kempers would still pick me up...

A barking dog interrupted my lineup of heavy-minded chores. My eyes focused on a corner of the ceiling where a spider was building his web. The barking was relentless.

Used with permission. cynoclub/Depositphotos.com

I shifted on the bench and sat up. Annoyed, I walked over to the small window and stretched my neck to see. The glass was not clear, it was frosted. Now, even more annoyed, I sat back down.

Minutes later, silence returned... the barking stopped so I laid on the bench and tried to get some sleep. I faded away... Sleep took me back to the beach with Anne, the seashells, the look in her eyes, her blonde hair flowing in the wind.

Time tick-ticked away. *The Kempers should be here any minute.*

But noon came and went. Then one o'clock. Then two. Hadn't Mom gotten ahold of them? Had they forgotten me?

Another hour passed... I paced the room like a caged animal. So far, it had been six hours of solitude. It was already 3:00 P.M. No word. No movement. No people. Not another human being...

The incessant barking started again. I cupped my ears. No use. Total torture. That dog must be hungry... *I'm hungry! Now I know how he feels.*

I continued to pace. It was almost time for me to go to work. Mr. Peters would be expecting me soon. My new boss was counting on me. He was going to think I was an awful kid.

Where were Jim and Terry? Did they go home without me?

Where was Sergeant Richardson?

What about Anne? She was going to think I was a jerk. She would think I didn't care. What about Mark? He was going to think I was a jerk, too. He'd wonder why I didn't meet him today.

I went to the door and yelled, "Hello, hello! Is anybody out there?" It was no use. No one could hear me.

Where was everyone?

"Hello," I tried again. The louder the dog barked, the louder I got. Still nothing.

After a few minutes I gave up. I raced across the room and shouted out the window, "Shut up! Go lay down."

Defeated, I slumped back on my bench. My elbows dropped to my knees. I held my head in my hands. I'd never even gotten a chance to congratulate Mark on his job.

I heard a squeaky voice in the hall.

"Who's there? Help!" I shouted with my face pressed against the window bars.

Within a minute the hall light came on. A gray-haired grandmotherly woman walked toward my door. "I thought I heard someone. I'm surprised to see you. What are you doing here?"

"Sergeant Richardson told me to wait here. Can I please speak with him?" I asked.

"Oh sonny, I think he's gone for the day," she said.

"I was supposed to get picked up at noon. I haven't had anything to eat or drink since nine o'clock this morning."

"Oh. Okay, honey. Don't worry. I'll see what I can find. I'll be back soon." Then she scurried away.

I flopped down on the wooden bed. My stomach churned. I looked up... *Thank you, God. Someone knows I'm here.*

With a little bit of hope I sat and waited. I enjoyed the calm. Even the dog stopped barking. It wasn't long before I heard steps coming in my direction. I jumped to my feet and hurried to go look.

"Hello, Larry. I've got some news... and some food," she announced.

I stepped aside. With a turn of the key she opened my door. She looked at me with soft caring eyes and gently handed me a tray.

"Thank you, ma'am." I took it over to the bench, looked down, and saw a peanut butter and jelly sandwich, a bag of chips, and a carton of milk. I sat it next to me.

"I was right, Sergeant Richardson is gone for the day. Officer Edwards is taking over. He found your folder. He's going to follow up and make some phone calls... It won't be long. Someone will be coming soon." She walked out of the room.

I relaxed for a few minutes, devoured the sandwich and chips, and downed the milk. Much better than the jail cell legends of bread and water.

I put the empty tray on the floor... and waited... and waited... and waited. What was taking them so long? I hoped she was right. I hoped I would get out of there soon.

Another hour passed. Then I heard voices in the hallway. In walked a uniformed officer and the woman who helped me. "Hi, I'm Officer Edwards. I see Mrs. Horn fed you."

The lady smiled and picked up the tray.

"Sorry for the mix-up. We didn't mean to keep you in this holding cell all day. Sergeant Richardson had another call and ran out. He didn't give us your folder. We had no idea you were even here. Looking through the paperwork, I only found a number for a Mrs. Schardt, which I'm assuming is your mother."

"Yes sir, it is."

"I've been trying to call but the line's been busy. As soon as I find out anything I'll let you know. Take it easy," he said.

Again I was alone. I sat, I laid, I paced. I sat, I laid, I paced... Fritz was probably on the phone talking to some girl, or Judy talking to some boy. This could be forever.

The evening sky darkened. The dread of spending the night in jail overtook my feelings of hope. Doing nothing but stressing all day had drained me. I walked my fatigued body back and laid down. My eyes closed.

Thoughts bombarded my mind. I wondered how mad Mr. Peters was when I didn't show. I wondered what Anne felt when she couldn't find me. I wondered if Mark still liked me.

The guilt of letting everyone down took a toll on me.

Where were the Kempers? Had their car broken down? Had they forgotten? What if they went home without me? My guilt twisted into a nightmare... What if Dad was the one coming to pick me up?

My tortured thoughts continued, but eventually I dozed off.

I was roused by a commotion of men talking in the hall. The light went on. I glanced at my watch. It was 11:30 P.M. I tried to recognize the voices. Was that my dad?

A stern male voice bellowed, "Wait here."

I laid still. My eyes focused on the bleak cinderblock walls that had held me captive for the past fourteen hours. Heavy footsteps echoed in procession to my chamber. The familiar key ring clattered. I sat up at abrupt attention.

A police officer walked in with a clipboard in his hand. "Hello, young man. Your friends are here to pick you up. Follow me."

Friends? Friends! I sighed in relief. Thank heavens it wasn't Dad! My tension blasted away in an instant. I couldn't get out fast enough.

There, at the end of the hallway, I saw two silhouettes. Jim and Terry came into sight as I got closer. I couldn't contain my Cheshire cat grin. *My saviors!*

I flashed them a peace sign and sniffed back the tears of joy. The atmosphere in the station was somber. The Kempers were unusually quiet so I followed their lead. Afraid of saying or doing the wrong thing, I kept my mouth shut. Jim had to play the part of being responsible for me. They probably wanted to get out the front door as much as I did.

Jim and Terry could have won an Academy Award for their role of being sober. Even I was convinced.

The officer asked, "Which one of you is over eighteen?"

Jim raised his arm. The officer motioned for him to come to the desk.

"This must be yours," the officer said as he handed me my tattered brown paper bag.

After Jim signed the papers, the officer began his lecture. "I am releasing him to you. Do you understand? He's now your responsibility. He is *not* to walk the streets of Ocean City alone. I'm talking the beach and boardwalk, too. You need to be with him at all times." He yammered on. "Remember, your friend is in your custody..." Blah, blah, blah.

Enough! I just needed to escape. His words were the only thing between me and freedom.

"Larry, I don't ever want to see your face again," he said.

At last. I broke through that final stronghold. I threw open the doors and raised my arms. "YES!"

On the way to the car, Jim said, "Hey man, how are you?"

"Great, now!"

"We were freaking paranoid. Couldn't wait to get out of there. Tomorrow we're going back to the 59th Street beach. Terry met this cool chick and he wants to see her again."

"Really? I fell in love with a chick named Anne on 9th Street. She's the most beautiful girl I've ever seen. I really need to see her one more time. Would that be okay?" I pleaded.

Used with permission. TAkhmet/Depositphotos.com

21 | Morning Dew

When we got to the Kempers' motel room on 7th Street, we sat on the two twin beds across from each other. Jim said, "Sorry it took us so long to get you out."

Terry interrupted, "These chicks wanted us to hang out with them today."

Jim continued the story. "Your mom must've called while we were on the beach, and the lady at the front desk told her we were staying an extra night. Man, from the message, it sounded like she was mad! She wanted you home so she could be sure you were safe."

I sighed. "It doesn't matter. I'm just glad you came for me and didn't go home without me. Thanks."

"Okay, tomorrow we're going back to 59th Street so Terry can see his sweetie again. I'd like to be out of town by two or three o'clock. What do you think?" Jim asked.

"Can we squeeze in a few minutes for me to see Anne one more time?" I pleaded.

"Let's see how much time we have," he said. "Okay?"

"Okay." I was disappointed by his indefinite answer.

Jim handed me a quilt from one of the beds. I stretched it out on the carpeted floor, and dropped my weary body into a corner. Jim and Terry talked in the background while I drifted to sleep.

Before I knew it the sun peered through the opening between the curtains. I knew what I had to do. I waited until the appropriate time.

At 8:10 I got up, dressed, scribbled a note saying, "I'll be back soon," and snuck out. I marched toward the boardwalk. Seagulls greeted me with their familiar squawking. I did my best to fade in with the early risers parading to the beach.

Mr. Peters was already opening his ice cream shop when I got there. Before I had a chance to say anything, he looked up, his face reddened. "What do you have to say for yourself?"

"I am so sorry. I was at the police station. I got caught."

"What do you mean you got caught?" He looked at me with concern.

My head lowered in shame. "I ran away from home in Pittsburgh and the police found me sleeping under the boardwalk yesterday morning. I spent the whole day in jail and now I have to go home. I didn't mean to upset you."

Mr. Peters said, "Well, young man, I'm sorry it didn't work out. Thank you for coming back and letting me know. Next time you're in Ocean City look me up for a job."

"Thank you, sir."

We sealed it with a handshake, and then he put his hand on my shoulder and said, "Good luck."

I wandered further down the boardwalk to the pavilion. I was dying to see Anne or Mark but they weren't there. The usual sweet, tempting scent of taffy circulated in the breeze.

I shuffled through the pavilion to say a melancholy goodbye to the ocean. I looked out across the sand, brightened by the morning sun, and filling with vacationers. I was transfixed by the rhythmic surf. So familiar. Yet so elusive. I replayed the days living in my temporary home, my journey, my friends, my love... knowing it was crashing to a halt.

An empty sense of longing drained from my head to my toes, like the waves backing across the beach. I noticed the stairs going down on my right. Just a few days earlier, I'd looked over to my flower child, the mystery goddess who'd captured my heart. Her peace sign, her smile, her charm...

A crooning seagull broke me out of my trance. *Dang, I'd better get back to the motel.*

When I got back, the Kempers were packing up. We threw the bags in the trunk and hopped into the car to head across Ocean City. We drove way up Asbury Avenue toward 59th Street, fifty-two long blocks away.

Terry was anxious. "Step on it. It's taking forever."

Jim obliged his brother and went a little over the twenty-five mile per hour speed limit. Eventually we got all the way to 57th Street when I heard a siren.

"Damn," Jim said as we pulled to the curb. "Let me do all the talking."

The uniformed police officer walked to the driver's window. I recognized his voice, and wanted to scrunch to the floor. It was the same officer who'd let me out of jail the night before and had told Jim he didn't want to see our faces again.

Maybe he wouldn't remember us.

Then he looked into the back seat.

No such luck. He remembered.

"You?"

Used with permission. appalachianview/Depositphotos.com

22 | Do You Believe in Magic?

"Didn't I tell you I didn't want to see you again?" the officer bellowed. "What's your hurry? I need your driver's license and registration."

Jim handed over his license while Terry searched the glove box for the registration. "I can't find it. It's not here."

"Sorry sir, we can't find it." Jim lowered his head.

The officer turned back to his police car to call in the information. I sat in the back seat sweating. I wanted to push Terry's seat forward, throw open the door, and run like crazy.

After an eternal wait, the officer approached the driver's window again. "I'm giving you a warning. Now go home!"

Without hesitation, Jim turned the steering wheel and pulled from the curb. "Damn, that cop's following us," he said. "Forget the beach, we've gotta go home."

After a few turns, he looked in the rearview mirror. We crawled along at twenty-five miles per hour.

"He's still following us." Jim glanced at the speedometer. With the cops on our trail, every block was sheer torture.

Annoyed, Jim looked to Terry. "No beach. No babes. We've got to get going."

Terry slumped and sulked. He made it no secret how he felt. The tension between the brothers thickened. I knew better than to ask about stopping back at 9th Street so I held my tongue.

After a dozen or so streets, a wail of sirens blasted. Jim pulled to the side of the road. The police car sped past.

Jim sighed. "Finally, he's gone." Our collective pressure valve released.

Terry said, "Come on, man. I've gotta see Patty one more time. I promised. You've got your love at home. Let me have a little love here. What's another half hour?"

"It's getting late already," Jim snapped. "Besides, will you ever see her again after today? Let's just freaking go!" After a long pause he gave in. "Okay, okay, but make it quick." He turned the car around and headed back to 59th Street.

We parked and walked the path to the beach. It was different from my "home beach"... no boardwalk, smaller crowd, and a long fishing pier. Nonetheless, there it was, the ocean once more... My eyes bulged when I saw a poster babe laying on a towel. *That must be Patty*, I thought. Like a roadrunner, Terry sped in her direction.

Jim yelled, "It's a long drive home and Mom's already pissed. That Philly traffic will be hell. You have thirty minutes! We'll sit over there." He pointed to an empty spot on the beach.

Jim and I sat. We watched Terry and held our own bikini judging contest.

Fifteen minutes passed until I built up my nerve. It was time when I saw Jim's veins un-pop from his neck. I knew a trip back to Shriver's to say goodbye would probably be out of the question but I needed to ask anyway. I swallowed and blurted out, "Can we please stop at 9th Street on our way out of town? I've just got to see Anne. I've got to apologize. It won't take long."

In that extended uncomfortable moment, I braced myself for his dreaded answer.

Jim gave me a fierce stare. "You guys are a pain in my ass with all this puppy love stuff. Okay, but make it quick. We're already way behind. If we get in any more trouble, you talk to the cop, you talk to my mom. No... talk to my dad!"

I looked over at Terry. My spirits lifted when I saw him stand up and get off the beach towel. He headed back in our direction.

"Great, let's get to 9th Street so this lover boy can say his goodbyes," Jim said. "Let's go."

We hopped into the car and after fifty long blocks arrived at the entrance to the boardwalk.

"Okay! Get going. If you aren't back in fifteen minutes, we're leaving without you, and don't think I won't!"

23 | She's Not There

I charged up the steps past the vacationers parading the boardwalk. The seagulls chattered their boisterous welcome. I hurried across the wooden boards to the pavilion. Tim was playing his guitar. The crowd was enjoying the music and humming to the tunes.

Once more, I flashed back to the day I'd arrived and the beautiful blonde flower girl who'd welcomed me to Ocean City with a smile and a peace sign.

I made my way around the pavilion, but there was no Anne... and no Mark... and no Jill. I looked across the beach to the ocean. Captivated for a moment or two, the gloom of hopelessness set in. My heart sank.

Then I looked over to my right and there they were in the distance—Mark, Jill, and... Anne! Sitting in a circle talking, they didn't notice me.

My feet couldn't move fast enough. I flew down the steps and plopped next to Anne. We didn't need to touch to feel the magical current flowing between us. Our smiles said everything.

"What the hell happened to you yesterday?" Mark asked. "We looked everywhere. We even went to your new job."

I tried to fit everything in as fast as I could. "Sleeping under the boardwalk" ... "Cops" ... "Holding cell" ... "Jim and Terry waiting for me in the car." I talked so fast I lost my breath. I inhaled the salty air.

Anne hung on to every word I said. She ran her finger slowly down my arm and when it reached my wrist, she took hold, bent down, and sweetly asked if I wanted to walk on the beach.

After half a block, she reached into her pocket and pulled out a photo. "Here, I was going to give you this yesterday. The phone number for our beach house is on the back."

I looked down at the picture of the gorgeous hippie girl I'd fallen for. My insides vibrated with excitement and over-whelmed my inhibitions. I leaned toward her and gave her a short but sweet kiss...

Then a surge of shyness flushed through me. I looked down at the sand.

"We should go back," Anne said. "They'll be looking for us."

I reached over and held onto her soft fingers. I didn't want to let go. We wove our way back, hand in hand, until we got to the boardwalk. Jim's car waited on the other side.

Mark's eyes opened wide. "Hey man, don't go. There's a guy I'm working with who's heading out to California at the end of the summer. He's going to drive us. Man, our dreams came true!"

A million thoughts surged through my brain. "Wow! Thanks, Mark." Were my dreams really finally coming true? Haight-Ashbury. Wow!

"Maybe I can come visit," Anne chimed in.

"Me too," Jill added.

I looked at Anne. I looked at Jill. I looked at Mark. The speed of my heart and my mind competed... sunny California becoming a reality... my ultimate goal. I wanted to dance with joy.

Away from Dad. *I won't have to face his wrath when I get home.* Away for good this time.

I turned and looked over the rail. Jim's Volkswagen was waiting. I'd made a promise to him. But he'd surely understand. I was torn. One part of me wanted to be responsible and go home, yet another wanted to stay free with my new friends and Anne. I wanted the whole dream.

Then I thought of my mom. After being all those miles away, her first words had been, *"You stinker."* Nothing screamed love like that.

I thought of Fritz, Judy, the twins, and the rest of my brothers and sisters. I thought of home. I thought of having a place to lay my head... and not having to beg.

Then back to Dad in my face, his angry frown scowling, his temper flaring.

"Thanks Mark, but I can't. I'm going home." My knees buckled as I continued to walk.

The smile vanished from Mark's face and his jaw dropped. "But it's your dream, man."

"I've got a new dream," I said, hoping I was making the right decision. "Maybe some other time." We gave each other the hippie handshake.

I hugged Jill goodbye, then I turned to Anne and held her in my arms. She put her head on my left shoulder. My eyes clouded. I fought back the tears.

"You better catch your ride," Mark reminded me.

I held Anne tighter. One final squeeze and I let go. I wanted to avoid looking into her watering baby blues.

I tore myself away and stepped toward the car.

"Be sure to call," she sobbed.

"Goodbye." I blew her a going away kiss.

I looked back for one last peace sign to my friends, to the ocean, and to Shriver's. Then I turned around and started the journey... "Homeward Bound."

I knocked on the car window and startled Terry. He climbed out so I could crawl into the cramped back seat.

"Perfect timing," Jim said. "Let's get going."

We pulled away from my ocean home and headed west toward the Garden State Parkway. I didn't look back. I couldn't. I watched the Ocean City restaurants, motels, and gas stations whiz by as we reached the bay. It was a final reminder that the Atlantic Ocean was now gone. The Great Egg Harbor Bay stretched forever in both directions dotted with buoys, boats, and strips of land.

24 | I'm Getting Closer to My Home

On the other side, the town of Somers Point bade us our last farewell as 9th Street funneled right onto the Parkway. The beach gave way to trees.

Jim and Terry's conversation was like a silent movie. Nothing registered. I held Anne's picture in my palm, taking a glimpse every few seconds.

I turned it over to see her number. There was a note too... "Looking forward to a great summer. Love, Anne."

My insides somersaulted. I was glad I was tucked in the back seat away from Jim and Terry. I pressed my lips together. I tasted a trace of strawberry gloss.

Terry popped *Abbey Road* into the 8-track player. "Something" was the soundtrack for my teenage love and angst. Memory took me back to that moment... a moment I never wanted to end. Her touch was embedded in my mind, everything about the way she moved. I didn't want to leave her now... or ever.

Then the should-haves attacked... *I should've kissed her again... I should've held her tighter... I should've hugged her one more time... I should've ... Maybe I should've taken Mark up on the offer...* And on and on.

The hum of the engine, my head in the love-clouds, and the miles and miles of identical pine forests lulled me into a trance. My eyelids drooped and I faded into a dream. Music played on and did battle with the unmistakable rat-tat-tat of the engine. I was out... back at the sea. Back at the beach. Back with Anne...

The Volkswagen's engine stopped, the music stopped, my dreams stopped. I woke to Jim's voice. "This sun is killing my eyes. I need a break."

I looked through the small back window. Terry jumped out, pushed his seat forward, and released me from my cramped quarters. We were at a rest stop on the Pennsylvania Turnpike.

Reality set in. New Jersey was behind us. The salt air had been replaced by diesel fumes. The pines gave way to dots of trees and farm fields. The evening sun was setting on my ocean dreams. A new chapter waited on the other side.

We shuffled into the Howard Johnson's restaurant. The smell of the grill welcomed us inside. We sat at a table and reminisced.

"I'm ready to go back," Terry said.

"Me too. Ah, sweet Anne." I wondered if I'd ever see her again.

Girls, girls, girls... love was on our minds.

The burgers, fries, and (this time) a Coke were delicious.

When we got back in the car, Jim turned to Terry. "We're going to be home in a few hours. We've got to get our story straight. What will we tell Mom?"

While they discussed their game plan, I sat in the back and shuddered. I knew that I didn't have to get my story straight. Dad wouldn't talk. Anguish of the inevitable smothered my dreams of bliss. I wanted to run back... to look at the ocean, to be free, to see Anne.

By the time we exited the turnpike onto the Pittsburgh Parkway in Monroeville it was around eleven o'clock. Terry tuned to KQV-FM to catch some more Rock music.

The steel stacks bellowed their smoky clouds into the dark sky, the molten slag glowing red as it flowed down the hillside, and the ever-present sulfur smell tainted the air—my warning of what was ahead.

We rounded the bend toward the Pittsburgh skyline. Grand Funk accompanied us with "I'm Getting Closer to My Home." My emotions zig-zagged, at once beauty, and at the same time terror. Every roll of the tires got us closer... to excitement, anticipation... then dread.

We crossed the Monongahela River on the Fort Pitt Bridge and funneled into the tunnel. Once we burst out the other side, my palms became sweaty. Ten minutes of freedom left. With every second the knot in my neck tightened.

By the time we drove past Mt. Lebanon High School I knew in a few minutes, I'd be walking through the door. I prepared as best I could for Dad's wrath. I made the worst out of what might be waiting for me.

We pulled into the Kempers' house around 11:30. Terry opened his door and climbed out. He pushed the seat forward and I wiggled my way out onto the driveway. Every muscle in my body ached. I stretched for temporary relief.

I looked at Anne's picture then tucked it into my pocket. I reached back into the car and grabbed my well-worn brown paper bag.

Jim walked over and put out his hand. "Good luck."

Terry did the same. "Yeah, good luck."

"Thanks. I'll need it. And thanks for the ride." I shuffled across the street to my house, every step heavier than the last.

The family car wasn't in the driveway. Maybe the coast was clear.

I paused at the beginning of the sidewalk and looked at my childhood home. I pulled out the black seashell, rubbing my fingers across its ridges. I put it back in my left bellbottom pocket.

When I got to the door, my body felt like lead. I expected anger, explosion, torment. I turned the knob and pushed open the door where Judy and Fritz stood waiting.

"Welcome home." Jude greeted me with a warm sisterly hug and Fritz joined in.

Dad wasn't home.

They waited up for me. The floodgates opened. I'd held it back for so long. My shoulders shook. I was home. Safe...

For the moment.

Used with permission. Syda_Productions/Depositphotos.com

25 | Hair

Every story needs a happy ending. That was mine. That night we hugged. Our faces were drenched with tears. I was home and home never felt so good.

But my happy ending was short lived.

Fritz said, "Come on upstairs. Let's get to bed."

"I'll be up in a minute. I need to grab a glass of water."

Moments later, Dad burst through the door fueled with the intense rage of alcohol... my worst enemy... and his worst enemy, too.

In a flash I got a backhand across my face. The force knocked me off balance. "You gawd damned son-of-a-bitch. What the hell were you trying to prove?"

For a moment, I froze. I almost ran out, but then I couldn't hold anything back... "I wasn't trying to prove anything. I was just trying to get away from *this!*" I shouted.

Dad glared. "Too bad the cops found you. I was hoping you'd never come back, you worthless bastard. Get up to your room now." He smashed me against the wall. "Now!"

"I'm trying," I mumbled.

"Not hard enough! Get going. First thing tomorrow, you're going to the barbershop." He shoved me in the back.

"I don't need a haircut. It's not even long."

"Shut up and get upstairs. I can't wait until you turn eighteen. You're out of here. I never want to see your face again. You understand?" I tripped on the first step when he shoved me again.

"Yes, sir," I said sarcastically. "I can't wait."

I crawled into bed, pain burning inside and out. I was grateful for a soft bed and a roof over my head. A pillow replaced my paper bag. Instead of Sergeant Richardson, I'd be seeing Mom after I delivered my papers. I held my seashell and fell into a dream where Anne took my pain away.

The next morning, at five o'clock, the alarm buzzed.

I swung out of bed, pushed the buzzer off, and began the formidable task of waking Fritz. Eric and Judy were shuffling around downstairs.

It was just like I'd never left. Had I really been gone? When I got to the kitchen, Eric and Judy were sitting at the table wolfing down their bowls of cereal.

Eric jumped up and greeted me with a hug. "I'm so glad you're home. We missed you." After a pause and a smirk, he went back to eating his breakfast. "Now we don't have to do your paper route anymore."

"Thanks, I appreciate you doing it for me," I said as I grabbed the box of sugary sweet Quisp cereal and joined them.

Like every morning we were in a rush to get out and deliver our papers... and like every morning, we waited for Fritz, who finally made it downstairs to join us.

"So what was the beach like?" Eric asked.

I rattled on. "It was amazing. I'm in love... The ocean was so cool... and there were beautiful girls in bikinis everywhere... Anne... Mark... Mr. Peters... The police..." I tried to jam as much in as I could before we had to leave for our *Post-Gazette* routes.

Judy asked, "Where'd you stay?"

"Porches... under the boardwalk... We hung out at a pavilion called Shriver's. If I can get Fritz's butt in gear, we're gonna meet Mom at the streetcar when she gets off."

Judy beamed. "Mom is going to be so glad to see you. I wish our routes were closer so I could see her face."

"Come on, Fritz," I grumbled. "Let's get going. Mom'll be there by 6:30. Please!"

After a few more minutes of infuriating putzing, all four of us headed out. We walked up the street together. At the top, Eric and Judy took off to the right for their route and Fritz and I turned left toward uptown Mt. Lebanon.

"Man, you should have seen her... and the ocean... and Shriver's candy store. Hey, they even had your favorite licorice."

Fritz nodded and his voice cracked. "I'm sure glad you're back. I missed you, man. Things just weren't the same. Everyone at the park was worried about you."

"They were?"

"Of course! They're gonna be so glad to see you. I'm so glad!"

Fifteen minutes later we were uptown. Fritz took off for his paper route and I took off for mine.

"Meet you at the trolley loop."

I raced around the Central Square apartment buildings and got the hundred or so papers delivered.

I ran to wait for Mom. I stood alone. The first trolley came along and Mom wasn't onboard. *Hope I didn't miss her!* I paced back and forth across the tracks.

Fritz got there just as the next streetcar came into sight. I stood breathless. When the car got closer, I saw Mom standing in the front. She walked down the steps onto the cobblestones.

"Larry!" She grabbed me in her arms.

My heart raced. "I'm sorry, Mom."

She just cried. She held on like she didn't want to let go. What a homecoming!

On the walk back to our house she asked me an endless list of Mom questions: "Where did you sleep? What did you eat? Where did you get money? Who did you meet?"

I shared tales of my journey but a bit more subdued than what I'd shared with Fritz. "I'm in love, Mom."

A smile crept across her face. I went on about Anne and love and Ocean City and Jersey.

Then she said, "I understand why you ran away. Please, don't ever do that again. You had me worried sick."

Remorse pumped through my veins. "I'm sorry," I said again.

She looked back at me. "I had a long talk with Dad. He's going to cut down on his drinking and start treating you better."

Huh? Sure didn't seem that way last night.

"He promised me he's going to get a job, too."

I wondered if she really believed it. I wished it might be true, but I couldn't see it. He'd never tried before.

When we got home, as usual, Dad was still in bed. After all, it was only seven. He wouldn't be awake for another four hours, at least.

Mom grabbed a cup of coffee. "Tell us more."

I rattled on about hitchhiking, John, getting a job, the ocean, the boardwalk. Mom shook her head a lot.

I passed around Anne's picture.

"Wow, Lar! She's beautiful," Judy said.

Fritz teased, "What in the world was she doing with *you?*"

I filled story-time at the Schardt's with vibrant new adventures. It was cool to be home, telling my stories, getting teased, and experiencing the lingering euphoria of my first summer love.

Our joy screeched to an abrupt halt when we heard Dad pounding down the back stairs.

Mom went into the kitchen to fix him breakfast.

After eating he stormed into the living room. "Time to get that damn hair cut. You gawd-damn hippie. Then we're going down to the new stadium to see if you can get a job." Dad's words thundered with fury.

"You mean *another* job," I snapped back.

"Get out to the car," he roared.

I hurried and climbed into the front seat. I sat as far away from Dad as I could. The arm rest dug into my side.

He peeled out, cussing and shouting the whole time. Every moment was a reminder of why I left in the first place. I looked out the side window, doing my best to keep my blood from boiling. With every quick turn he made, the arm rest pushed deeper into my side.

A dreaded haircut... the last thing I needed or wanted. Hair was the outward sign that made me different from him... and I sure didn't want to be anything like him.

I felt like a prisoner. Trapped. I wanted to throw open the door and take off.

But the agony I felt was not as strong as the love I'd been missing... family, friends, a roof over my head, and a soft bed to sleep in every night. And food... I had food!

But mostly I had love... No matter what my father said, no matter how he said it, and no matter what he did, I knew I cherished my family more than my independence. What a blessing to be loved!

Epilogue
Eternity Road...
The Balance

The Summer of 1970 was a lifetime ago.

Time... As the years accumulated, my curiosity about life deepened. I could never understand how people were so different, even people raised under the same roof. Why were some angry? Why did some want adventure? Why were some content to be complacent? Why were some mean and others kind?

I realized that the one and only person I could control was me. I am 100% responsible for my own life, my own success, my own happiness. It wasn't up to my dad, or my mom, or my job, or my lover. It was totally up to me.

I wanted to understand. Why was my father so angry?

How could I expect my dad, or anyone, to change? It was hard enough to run my own life, let alone expect someone else to do it for me. If I'd waited for my dad to change in order for me to be happy, I would have had a miserable life.

I've been studying happiness and success all my adult life. (Check out my daily Facebook posts.) I want to rock my life and the lives of others with success... Success That Rocks!

Happiness has a profound effect on success. The happier you are, the more successful you become. We cannot control others. I could never control my dad any more than he could control me. If I wanted to promote peace, love, and kindness in life, I realized I would have to take responsibility and practice what I preached.

Peace, love, and kindness start at home.

I looked into my dad's life and did my best to walk a mile in his shoes. I learned he'd risked his life in World War II. He

121

stormed Normandy Beach. He liberated Paris. He was on the front lines across Europe... He even suffered through the brutal Battle of the Bulge. He fought! He endured! He persisted! He put his life on the battle lines to save every human in the free world.

Yet he never thought of himself as a hero. He came home with the lifelong scars of (unknown at the time) PTSD and depression. He did his best to self-medicate with alcohol, which only intensified his pain.

Back in the '50s, '60s, and '70s most men were ashamed to seek (much needed) therapy. My dad was one. His life was hell and he took it out on me. I never want to see another child or person be abused, physically or mentally. Thank heavens for therapy and safe havens to protect the innocent. Running away is not the answer!

When I put the pieces together I understood a lot, and my heart opened.

No matter what, I am the person I am today because of what happened. We always have a choice in life... to learn compassion and love, or hang on to anger and carry bitterness. With every ending is a new beginning. Yes to love... and no to turmoil.

In the words of Martin Luther King, Jr., "I have decided to stick with love. Hate is too great a burden to bear."

In my adult years, my father and I became great friends, a gift I am forever grateful for. He got a job and began working in the late '70s. We shared endless stories and laughs.

Through those stories and laughter we began to understand each other in ways my fifteen-year-old self could never have imagined. What a blessing to see him in a more complete way... with the eyes of understanding.

Thanks, Dad.

Photo by author. My Dad. My friend.

The Woodstock Nation and the Age of Aquarius are memories now but still live in the hearts of those who perpetrate peace, love, and kindness. The ideals of the Love Generation will never end. Magic fills the air... when you make it happen. There is always beauty in Flower Power.

Rock 'n' Roll is my soundtrack for appreciating life and celebrating joy. It's the perfect antidote for corporate, commonplace, mass-produced music. Rock 'n' Roll is the prescription for hope and good and for those who refuse to sell out to "The Man." Rock 'n' Roll helped me get through the good times and the bad. Long live Rock!

Decades have passed since that fateful runaway summer. I was fortunate to survive. So many things could have gone wrong. I was spared only by the grace of God.

The ideals of the Love Generation made a permanent home in my heart.

Through the years, life constantly reinforced the fact that it's my own responsibility to create happiness and success... and share it with others.

I am forever blessed to have memories that carry the spirit with me. Thank you for sharing that spirit. Thank you for sharing that fateful summer, when I was fifteen and alone... My Runaway Summer.

Many blessings...
Peace, Love, and Rock 'n' Roll!!!

Author Larry Schardt. Ocean City, NJ boardwalk.

My Back Pages

Thank You and a Favor...

Thank you for joining me on the journey back to 1970. If you loved the trip, and have a few moments, I would greatly appreciate a short review on Amazon, Goodreads, or your favorite social media. This helps other potential readers find my book.

With a Little Help
from My Friends...
(and a Whole Lotta Love)

This book was not a solo effort. Even though I took the physical journey, I had friends who lived vicariously through the mental parts and cheered me on. First and foremost, I'd like to thank God. Thank you for the adventures and always watching over me, now as then, especially through the turbulent times.

Thanks to my family for the incredible gift of love. You continually help me through the rough spots in life... cemented by the bonds of love and friendship (peppered with a heavy dose of teasing). God bless Mom, Dad, Eddie, Jude, Fritz, Eric, Keith, Davo, Marita, and Mary, and my newer (to me) wonderful family members Ed and Cherie.

Thank you to the wonderful friends who inspected, edited, and polished the many drafts, especially Kathleen Shoop, Christine Berliner, Barbara Hyde, and her cool mother Phyllis (Hyde) Hanus. An extra special thanks to my sweetheart, Gail Brittenburg, for her tireless support and ceaseless editing, polishing, and encouragement.

Endless thanks to Demi Stevens, my publisher, editor, book shepherd, and friend. Her extraordinary encouragement and patience kept me going. God bless Demi for putting up with my seemingly never-ending polishing and changes.

Thank you to the amazing friends who cheered me on throughout the process, including Facebook friends who followed this story and encouraged me to develop it into the book you now hold.

I am grateful for the incredible writers who make the Mindful Writers Retreats rock. Writing in the collective spirit with phenomenal authors is a miraculous gift. Many thanks to the phenomenal staff at the Ligonier Camp and Conference Center, who highlight the empowering spiritual setting of the Laurel Highlands.

A special thanks to my mastermind group: The Joy Hil Rockers, who have encouraged and supported me through many years of life adventures.

A big thanks to the Pennsylvania Turnpike Commission and Christine (Chrissy) Bennett, who not only granted permission to use historical photos, but helped me locate some amazing ones in the archives. *Special note: The photo of the Howard Johnson's counter was the exact spot where I met Eric and Joe.*

I would also like to thank the Ocean City Police Department... Vickie Ballezzi, Sergeant Tom Schmidt, and Patrolman John Simpsin... who were most kind and generous with their help. Thanks to the original officers and staff who probably kept me from a life of homelessness... and gave me my first cooked meal since I left home.

Thanks to the volunteers and staff at the Ocean City Historical Museum: Al and Sandy Crescenzo, Karl Wirth, Carol Dotts, and Jackie.

Additional thanks to photo contributors at Pixabay, DepositPhotos, and Jack Freeman of Longport, NJ.

Way back thanks to... Bill Ericson, The No Church Church, Mrs. Sullivan (not her real name), John (not his real name), Jim and Terry Kemper, Mark, Eric and Joe (not their real names), Anne (not her real name and forever lost in time), the kind girls who let me "crash" at their pads (on their porches).

Special thanks to the Woodstock/Love Generation and the hippies who continue to live the ideals of peace, love, and kindness.

The stars aligned at the dawn of the Age of Aquarius. The spirit was perfect. The music was perfect. The mood was perfect. The love was perfect.

Thanks to the musicians who provided the perfect soundtrack for life.

And thanks to those special times and places... The magical time known as the '60s and early '70s (aka The Love Generation), the Greatest Generation, Pittsburgh, Mt. Lebanon, "The Park," "The Circle," The Jersey Shore, Ocean City, Cape May, Wildwood, Stone Harbor, Avalon, Shriver's, and the millions of vacationers who make the area special.

About the Author

Photo Credit: Penn State University

Dr. Larry Rock 'n' Roll!!! Schardt (pronounced Shard) is on a journey of discovering and sharing the power of living a life of happiness and Success That Rocks. Larry's passion is people. He's been studying human behavior since he was a boy. As the oldest of eight, he's had lots of practice.

For over thirty-five years, Larry has entertained audiences across the United States encouraging, motivating, and inspiring executives, employees, students, and seniors to live life to the fullest. During that time, he has taught at multiple universities and is approaching his thirtieth year at Penn State.

Larry believes you have the ability to make your life rock... and as a result, to rock the lives of those you come into contact with. He greets everyone with exuberance, the peace sign, and his favorite salutation, "Rock 'n' Roll!!!"

He co-coordinates the highly successful Mindful Writers Retreats, and in 2019, wrote the bestseller, *James Conner: Legend of a Football Hero.* Connor, too, overcame adversity and epitomizes the rewards of hard work, kindness, humility, caring for others, and the sincerity of sharing a genuine smile. The book was rated "One of the 24 Best Sports Biography Books of All Time," according to BookAuthority (featured on CNN, and *Forbes* and *Inc* magazines).

Since 2015, Larry has been writing a daily Facebook blog to entertain, celebrate, share, and pay forward the good things in life. He feels everyone should start their day on a positive note.

Along with Larry's other writings, his inspiring stories appear in the *Chicken Soup for the Soul* books: *Find Your Happiness*, *The Power of Gratitude*, and *The Best Advice I Ever Heard*.

In his writing and everyday pursuits, Larry's passion for people, positive spirit, and zest for life shine through. He loves the outdoors, walking, reading, skiing, and music that rocks... from classical to Rock 'n' Roll.

Please Connect and Stay in Touch

Larry@SuccessThatRocks.com
SuccessThatRocks.com

amazon.com/author/larryschardt

facebook.com/Larry.Schardt

twitter.com/LarrySchardt

linkedin.com/in/larryschardt

PS - I Love You

Please email Larry@SuccessThatRocks.com
for bonus content.

"Answering the unanswered questions..."

"Lessons learned from the road."

Made in the USA
Middletown, DE
27 June 2023

33942082R00080